LINDA BRETHER'

The Creators Name

_____

Date_____

# LINDA BRETHERTON

'how fast can you change your life?'

'learn the rules··· play the game···
you have nothing to lose and absolutely everything to gain'

www.thecreatinggame.com

*Create with intent*
*Create on the edge*
*Create hard*
*Create your health*
*Create your love*
*Create with abandon*
*Create without regret*
*Create what you love*
*Create your life*

*Vani*

The Creating Game © how fast can you change your life?
Copyright © 2006 Linda Bretherton. All rights reserved.
Printed and published in United Kingdom by Learning Partnerships

ISBN 978-0-9552937-0-2      0-9552937-0-7

Cover illustrated by Philip Bretherton
First edition 2006

Linda Bretherton

# The Creating Game©

*"We were born to create! Go ahead bite the 'apple of knowledge' and co-create with the Universe!"*

*Vani*

*"You are going to create your future!*
*We are going to play this game together.*
*It's the game of life and its going to be fun."*

*Vani*

# Contents

"We are beings that were destined to know great movement or motion. Our energy was meant to be transformed into experiences. If you have not yet chosen to use the energy of life, and the energy of the universe, to reform and reshape your world, you are in a state of stagnation."

Jack Boland

# Foreword

"Vani (Linda) has been blessed with a gift from heaven...The first time Vani held my hands I could literally and physically feel the energy cycling through my own body. What happened in my own life over the following months...was that anything which was discordant, and no longer served me, could no longer exist in my life anymore. Her gift doesn't end there, she has also learned the language around her energy. Major shifts started happening to me, which allowed me the opportunity to serve myself in the highest ways possible. Working with her became crucial for me in sorting through the shifts that were taking place (some rapidly and others more subtly). Her incredible insight and knowledge is like a sword of truth cutting through all the crap my ego wanted to believe, straight through to divine truth and love. I went from a caterpillar to a butterfly in those months and I don't know that I could have made that personal metamorphosis without her example, love, support, knowledge, guidance, truth and joy. I went from an overweight, broke, housewife of 7 children, with a cheating husband... to a slim beautiful goddess, living in a gorgeous home, with a new man in my life that treats me in a manner I never knew possible, living my purpose in abundance, love, joy, light, freedom, truth, beauty - these things are our true nature, these are the things in which we simply are. Vani understands this and assists people as they self-actualize their true potential. She is truly a light worker in the greatest sense of the word. She assists people in 'self actualisation' shining a light on them and magnifying who they are and where they are, so that they are able to make shifts in their lives. Thank you my beautiful, dear sister!"

The Creating Game is a simple yet profound tool Vani has created; assisting people in making their highest dreams come true. Not only will you enjoy this beautiful little book, but you will be able to utilize Vani's gift as if you were working with her directly. Heaven is right here on this earth, it's simply a choice away. Choose to live your heaven in creating your highest dreams today by working with this divine book.

Thank you my beautiful, dear sister!"

*Lisa Clapier*
*Author, Sacred Destiny*

*"What lies behind us and what lies before us are tiny matters compared to what lies within us."*

Oliver Wendell Jones

# Introduction to The Creating Game

This book is about learning to create what you truly want in life, learning to play the game of creating. It is a game that can be mastered and perfected the more you play it. The Creating Game is based upon the premise that anyone can create what ever they truly desire. It can be played by anyone, of any age, class, gender or culture. There are no exceptions and everyone has the chance to play and succeed beyond their wildest dreams. You do not actually need to believe that you can create – in fact the Law of Creation, as explained in many self help books and also one of the most well-known sources of guidance, the Bible, simply tells you that you are already creators in the game of your life. Where you are today is exactly how you have created it, whether you have been conscious in the way you have played your life game or not. People are often not aware that they are already creating exactly what they desire so they create their lives unconsciously. All you need to know is that if you are willing to follow this game plan you will be able to become **conscious** creators and change your life.

In busy day-to-day lives you react to your world and outside influences determine the way you live and behave. This can affect the things you desire. Make a commitment to follow through with this game and you can and will become co-creators working in collaboration with the vast universal energy of the Law of Attraction in all that you choose to do. To make this happen you simply need to put these practices into action.

I remind people in my work shops that they cannot fail at being the creators in their lives because that is what they already are! It is impossible to fail at this game; you may not get it right the first time, but if you are truly willing to examine yourself and committed to what you truly desire to create in your life, then you will do it!

This book allows you to follow sequential activities. The format enables you to examine and therefore become aware of your own limiting behaviours, stumbling blocks and resistances. The Game will also enable you to identify the true underlying desires and patterns that rule your life today and then to take simple, direct steps to accept that behaviour for what it was and alter it to serve you better. To take part in the Creating Game doesn't mean you will need to spend a great deal of time analysing, postulating, feeling guilty, connecting with your shame or delving deeply into your past mistakes, problems or behaviours. You will recognise your patterns and set new ones.

The Game will encourage you to enter into a process of enquiry which leads to self discovery, reviewing, recapping and a summarising of your life to date.

This book addresses the one creation that you wish to bring into being at any one time, so that you can gain the greatest benefit from all the activities required to achieve your objective. You should fill in each and every page of this book for one specific creation. Do not attempt to do a variety of different creations at any one time. It is my experience that those who do this fail before they can get a handle on creating, because they become overwhelmed.

The format has been chosen so that you can monitor your progress, expand your awareness and grow and evolve into a magnificent creator of all that you desire. You should purchase a new copy of this book for every new creation until you are so proficient at creating you do not need to work in a game book. After many years of playing The Creating Game I still go back to the basics. There is always something to see, learn, remember and reinforce when playing the Game. Many of you have life long patterns of sabotage, lack of self worth and uncertainty that rarely leave you completely free of their influences. Taking part in The Creating Game or any other practice doesn't make these patterns go away; you simply become more aware of your own tendencies, making them less limiting so that it's easier to then strive to move on from where you are stuck.

It may seem extravagant to suggest you use a new book for each of your creations, but is not. Your creations are valuable and worthy of receiving complete and individual attention. If you do not consider your creation a precious and desirable idea in its own right , then no one else will either and you will be unlikely to succeed. It is important to dedicate an individual place for each creation you choose and The Creating Game book is the perfect special place to give your creation its identity. One of the main reasons you have found it difficult to create what you desire is that any creation requires clear, determined, specific and loving attention all the way from its conception until it is birthed in your life. Only by placing your intentions in a central position in your consciousness can they be achieved. When that happens, which it will, then you can celebrate its arrival and your great achievement in manifesting it into being. Your creation is precious, important, desirable, special, divine, and exquisite and completely yours. That is why it requires its own unique book.

Do not underestimate the importance of doing all the exercises on all the pages every time you choose to play a new game. It is crucial to perfecting the game and expanding your creating abilities for you to do the exercises each time, even though you think you have already completed them more than once or twice. If you do what is suggested at the beginning of each exercise I guarantee you will find new things to express in your creation book. See this little gem as a journal of expression as well as a creating book and you will gain valuable insight about the way you see things. This will strengthen your ability to develop clearer creations and therefore bring them into being more effectively.

If you decide to start the game of creating today you will encourage and encounter an energy that will work immediately in your favour, setting your creation in motion. To do this you should set aside the time to fill in each page and move through the exercises relatively quickly. Reading through the book quickly first and then completing each exercise in one or two sessions will in fact lend strength and momentum to your creation. You must of course ensure you follow the Game plan, and do not skip any section that you feel uncomfortable with. Continue to recapitulate and reaffirm, as will be explained throughout the creative process. I advise you not to expand or change the recommendations in 'The Creating Game', as this will only lead to disappointment. Those who choose to change these plans rarely join the co-creative team who commit to designing the best life they can. Your creation should have a three month time scale, no longer. It can and often will become shorter as a result of the energy that you release once you fully commit to completing the Game. You should use this book to take you through the full 3 month period and if you follow this game plan you will experience a new energy that leads you to empowerment and success.

You will notice throughout the book that I have introduced and suggest you use EFT (Emotional Freedom Techniques) after certain activities. You don't need to use it, the choice is yours, but it is an incredibly effective process. I absolutely love to use it as it is so simple, valuable and safe. In the Appendix you will find an introduction to EFT and what is called the Basic Recipe so that you can start to use it straight away if you choose to. It is advisable to read the completed instructions first and these can be obtained from the founder's website. A vast amount of information regarding EFT can be located there and details are in the Appendix.

What makes The Creating Game unique is that it constantly encourages you to move through the activities quickly without dwelling on 'painful' issues and thus losing your drive and impetus. You are encouraged to acknowledge these issues but the intention is to flow through the exercises and continually bring your self to a centred and relaxed state for the act of creating. You are given 'focus points' throughout, you could see these focus points as acts of intention that reaffirm what you are doing. You will be constantly reminded of these as you are lead through each activity. Do not be tempted to pass over any of the focus reminders that accompany the exercises. You will benefit greatly in motivation, excitement, ease, determination and persistence if you practice these simple reminders.

You will also find 'insight' boxes where you are encouraged to capture with your own comments, insights, feelings and responses. Many of the activities have empty facing pages for your answers and feelings regarding the activity. In all the places where you are asked to write, stop before you respond and be willing to answer and describe how you feel about what is happening to you as well as answering the actual questions.

Later on when you begin to create your desires it will be invaluable for you to look back at the comments you have made. So don't hold back, allow yourself to be as expressive as you can.

You will also notice that as you work through the exercises your feelings will change and you will find it easier to express them on the page. Welcome to the Game!!

---

**INSIGHT** ( HOW DO YOU FEEL AFTER READING THE INTRODUCTION? )

---

## Words of caution

When you engage in The Creating Game you will enter into a process of enquiry that will lead to genuine self discovery. In my experience individual self enquiry is also self regulating and self caring. This means that in some cases you will only ever 'go on your journey' to the extent that you are capable of accessing, at this moment in your life.

How ever if you find that you have experiences that are too difficult for you to process you must take responsibility and care for your self. You should make a choice whether you will visit your doctor or therapist to support you.

This book does not replace any medication or medical practice that you may be taking or need.

# Game Guidelines

At the start of each activity you will need to take a couple of minutes to find stillness and tap into your inner guidance. In all my years of working with people either in workshops or as individuals, anyone who has been reluctant to do this at the beginning of each activity has missed out on the possibilities of increased knowledge and awareness. Quiet time and inner silence enables us to clear confused thoughts and any nagging doubts that we may have about helping our process.

The Creating Game is not about teaching you to visualize, meditate, do breathing exercises or practice yoga, but I can guarantee that your creations will manifest much more quickly if you do at least develop a meditation practice. I have found that people have many reasons and excuses for not doing such simple work and once questioned it really comes down to the fact that they do not believe they have any effect. My response is always 'what have you got to lose'. These practices are ancient and go back to the past where this wisdom was practiced for the good of humans and the earth.

Here are some simple guidelines to follow to connect to your inner voice.

- TAKE A MOMENT TO SIT UP STRAIGHT WHERE EVER YOU MAY BE, THIS WILL SUBLIMINALLY INSTRUCT THE BODY AND MIND TO CONNECT IN THE PARTNERSHIP OF CREATING

- CLOSE YOUR EYES AND TAKE THREE SLOW, EVEN AND DEEP BREATHS

- LET YOUR SELF BE OPEN TO ANY ANSWERS THAT YOU RECEIVE, WITHOUT JUDGEMENT

- RELAX THE BODY, CHECK SHOULDERS AND FACE FOR TENSION AND TIGHTNESS

- ASK THE SPECIFIC QUESTION THAT IS PROVIDED AT THE BEGINNING OF EACH ACTIVITY. YOU CAN USE THE WORDS SUGGESTED OR MAKE UP YOUR OWN

- AFTER YOU HAVE WAITED A MOMENT STOP AND LISTEN TO THE FIRST THING THAT COMES INTO YOUR HEAD

- DO NOT ANALYSE THE ANSWERS OR MAKE THEM FIT WHAT YOU REALLY THINK YOU WANT TO HEAR

You may be surprised at what you hear, and may have the same old issues coming back again and again. This is not a bad sign. What it will do is help you to see how your inner chatter is programmed to say the same things. Understanding this will help you to connect with your energy and to either let it go or to embrace it depending on what serves you best at this time. You will have many opportunities to listen to your inner voice and to enter your experiences into the insight boxes.

# Time Scales

I am often asked about timescales for completing a creation and below are my guidelines.

- FROM THE MOMENT THAT YOU PURCHASED THIS BOOK YOU EMBARKED ON A PROCESS THAT SET INTO MOTION THE POTENTIAL AND SPACE FOR CREATING

- READ THROUGH THE CREATING GAME BOOK QUICKLY YET THOROUGHLY BEFORE YOU BEGIN ANY EXERCISE

- SPEND NO LONGER THAN FOUR WEEKS TO WORK THROUGH ALL THE ACTIVITIES, BEFORE CHOOSING YOUR CREATION

- EACH ACTIVITY SHOULD TAKE NO LONGER THAN A DAY OR TWO TO COMPLETE AND ASSIMILATE. YOU CAN COMPLETE MORE THAN ONE IN A DAY.

- PLEASE COMPLETE ALL FOCUS POINTS AND INSIGHTS TO GAIN THE BENEFITS FOR THE CREATIVE PROCESS

- THE CREATION THAT YOU CHOSE SHOULD BE CHOSEN AND MANIFESTED WITHIN A THREE MONTH PERIOD. THIS MEANS THAT YOU SHOULD NOT TRY TO CREATE SOMETHING THAT WILL TAKE A LIFE TIME TO ACHIEVE FOR EXAMPLE 'TO BE HAPPY', OR 'TO BE PEACEFUL'. THESE ARE LIFE LONG CREATIONS AND YOU BUILD UPON THEM CONTINUALLY.

- WHEN YOU CHOSE YOUR CREATION IT IS IMPORTANT THAT YOU BELIEVE IT WILL BE POSSIBLE TO CREATE IN THREE MONTHS. CREATING WORKS FOR YOU WHETHER YOU BELIEVE IT OR NOT. BUT IT IS MUCH EASIER FOR YOU TO LEARN THE CREATING GAME WITH SHORT CREATIONS TO GAIN CONFIDENCE AND MOMENTUM. YOU WILL THEN BE ABLE AND MORE WILLING TO ASK FOR GREATER THINGS. ONLY CHOSE CREATIONS AT THIS STAGE THAT WILL FIT INTO A THREE MONTH TIME SCALE.

- WHEN YOU REACH THE MY CREATION CHAPTER AND HAVE COMMITTED TO A CLEAR AND PRECISE CREATION YOUR THREE MONTH MANIFESTATION PERIOD BEGINS.

- CONTINUE GOING THROUGH THE CREATING GAME BOOK AS YOU BRING YOUR CREATION INTO BEING.

- IF YOU CHOSE YOU WILL BE ABLE TO COMPLETE THREE NEW CREATIONS IN TWELVE MONTHS AND MORE AS YOUR MOMENTUM AND ABILITY INCREASE

- CREATING WORKS FOR YOU WHETHER YOU BELIEVE IT OR NOT.

- HAVE FUN!

# At Your Core

There are some activities that require a little more quiet time - perhaps a few extra minutes. This first activity 'At Your Core' is an example of one of these. The questions posed demand attention and respect. This one will set your creative juices flowing, opening up the areas within you that will help you to create.

You will need to answer two questions in this activity

---

- WHAT MAKES YOU FEEL GOOD

- WHY DOES IT MAKE YOU FEEL GOOD

---

It is important again not to analyse these questions because we are looking for your instinctive responses. This can be more difficult than it first appears. I once worked with a student, who we shall call Jack, who simply would not answer any question straight away no matter how I encouraged and urged him. He had spent his whole life making sure that what he did or said was what he thought was expected of him. He had to be sure that he had the correct answer so that he could look good, sound correct, not upset anyone or give the answer he thought I was looking for. He did not want to look stupid, or to be embarrassed. He wanted to be 'the nice guy'.

After doing the activities several times he found that his thought process rarely made him feel genuinely good. Everything he did had an ulterior motive, which was not about his own true desires but about complying with others. Until then this series of lies he had built around his communication did enable him to 'think' he was a 'good bloke'. After uncovering this pattern he was able to see clearly that his own true needs were not being met. Jack set about creating the things that he wanted and not what others wanted.

All you ever want is to feel good about yourself, no matter how it is expressed in your daily life. At your deepest you want to feel good. Everything you do whether it seems like self abuse, starving yourself to be thin. sleeping around, eating comfort food, working too hard, winning in arguments, drinking too much, smoking, buying more clothes than you can wear, behaving in ways to get attention, regardless of what you are doing, you do it to feel better.

The biggest stumbling block with this is that very few people really know at their core what it is that makes them feel good for any sustained length of time. The only way that feeling good would have any real enduring meaning is if this feeling is built on a proper foundation.

A new coat, car, computer game will only last as long as the next new one. This is what makes marketing so effective; it continually provides you with all the material things you think will make you happy. And for a little while it does! The trouble is that it is also a "beast" that continually needs to be fed and leaves you constantly looking for something else to help you feel good about yourself.

At the beginning of the process you will need to 'shine' a light on what you actually believe about your happiness, contentment and the way you feel about your life. You will need to do this before you can learn the game of creating. Skipping any step will be detrimental to your creation. There are different internal exercises that will help you to tap into your inner creative guidance; each one is a proven way to increase creative practice. Start by doing the following:

---

- TAKE A FEW MINUTES TO SETTLE YOUR BODY AND YOUR MIND.

- PUT BOTH FEET ON THE FLOOR AND TAKE THREE SLOW AND EVEN BREATHS.

- FEEL YOUR BOTTOM AND UPPER THIGHS IN THE CHAIR WHERE YOU ARE SITTING. THIS IS YOUR BASE CHAKRA AREA, THE BODY'S SEAT AND FOUNDATION. THIS IS THE PLACE THAT HOLDS THE SECRETS OF YOUR CORE BEING. (A BRIEF DESCRIPTION ON THE CHAKRAS IS FOUND IN THE APPENDIX) HOW YOU FEEL ABOUT YOURSELF IN THIS WORLD AND WHAT REALLY MAKES YOU FEEL WHOLE AT A VERY DEEP LEVEL IS FOUND THROUGH THE BASE CHAKRA. EVEN IF YOU DO NOT UNDERSTAND OR BELIEVE THIS, GO AHEAD ANYWAY. YOU CAN COME TO NO HARM AND YOU MAY BE SURPRISED AND LEARN SOMETHING NEW. (THERE ARE MANY BOOKS AVAILABLE ON THE CHAKRA SYSTEM IF YOU WANT TO EXPLORE HOW THESE AMAZING SYSTEMS OF BODY VORTICES WORK WITHIN YOU IN MORE DETAIL)

- AS YOU PAY ATTENTION TO THIS LOWER BODY AREA PUSH YOURSELF DOWN A LITTLE INTO THE CHAIR SO THAT YOU CAN FEEL SOME PRESSURE THERE; REALLY GET IN TOUCH WITH YOUR BASE.

- NOW TRY TO IMAGINE A DEEP RED COLOUR THAT GLOWS FROM YOUR BASE AREA. IMAGINE THAT YOU'RE SITTING ON A DEEP RED GLOWING CUSHION AND FEEL THE WARMTH AND THE SENSE OF SECURITY THIS WILL BRING.

- NOW IMAGINE YOURSELF AT A MUCH YOUNGER AGE. GO AS FAR BACK AS YOU CAN AND ASK YOURSELF THESE QUESTIONS –

    o   WHAT REALLY MAKES ME FEEL HAPPY?

    o   WHAT TOUCHES ME AND BRINGS ME JOY?

    o   WHAT HAS BROUGHT ME DEEP LOVE AND SATISFACTION?

---

Let your mind flow a little as you allow the true essence of what makes you feel happy to emerge. Do not be concerned about what comes from this exercise; what ever it is, accept it. There are no right, wrong, perfect or standard answers and whatever comes will be just for you. If you find yourself becoming emotional don't be afraid, in fact celebrate that you are getting in touch with your deeper self. This can often be an emotional and liberating feeling as you are able to turn inwards for answers to deep questions and receive replies based on exactly what you need right now.

Do not attempt to make any answers into something they are not but simply listen to what comes to you. If you have difficulty getting any answers, try to look at how you feel at that moment. Are you anxious, sceptical or fearful?

Acknowledge these feelings by expressing them out loud to yourself and then recommit and do the exercise again. You might say, 'Ok this feels really weird but it can't do me any harm and it will only take me 5 minutes, so come on, get on with it!'

## Focus Point

Close your eyes and take three, deep slow breaths and explore your thoughts and mental images. What do you day dream about? What thoughts do you have? Imagine for a short while about this chapter and see where your thoughts lead you. Try to follow your process of thinking. Notice if your thought process in this example leads you in a positive direction or negative direction.

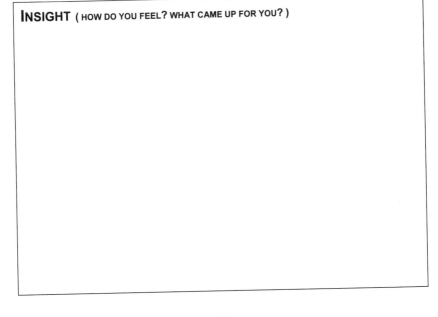

INSIGHT ( HOW DO YOU FEEL? WHAT CAME UP FOR YOU? )

# A Positive Sense of Self

When Jack, in the last chapter, looked at what was really happening behind what he believed helped him to feel good, he found that his life felt empty without the reactive 'pleasing' he had always adopted. These and other issues covered up any real sense of self worth.

- WITHOUT A POSITIVE SENSE OF SELF YOU FEEL LOST AND EVEN IN A FULL TIME RELATIONSHIP YOUR SENSE OF FULFILMENT CAN BE LACKING.

- EVEN IN A SUCCESSFUL ENVIRONMENT YOUR SENSE OF WORTHINESS CAN BE LACKING. IT FEELS LIKE SOMETHING'S MISSING.

- NO AMOUNT OF MATERIAL OBJECTS OR PEOPLE CAN MAKE YOU INTO A SELF-CREATING BEING.

- THE KEY TO CREATING IS YOUR AWARENESS ABOUT YOURSELF AND KNOWING WHAT IT IS YOU TRULY WANT.

- OFTEN YOU CAN FEEL THAT YOUR LIFE IS EMPTY AND THIS CAN BE A METAPHOR THAT DESCRIBES YOUR SENSE OF SELF AS BEING EMPTY.

- YOU CAN MEASURE YOUR OWN SUCCESS BY HOW 'GOOD' YOU ACTUALLY FEEL ABOUT YOURSELF ON A CONSISTENT BASIS.

- YOUR LIFE IS EMPTY TO THE DEGREE IN WHICH YOU CREATED IT TO BE EMPTY.

- YOUR LIFE FEELS EMPTY BECAUSE YOU HAVE CREATED PATTERNS THAT CONTINUE TO REINFORCE A LACK OF SELF WORTH.

- YOUR BEHAVIOUR, WHAT YOU SAY, WHAT YOU EAT, HOW YOU EAT, WHO YOU INTERACT WITH, WHERE YOU GO, HOW YOU WORK, HOW YOU LIVE AT HOME AND IN YOUR SURROUNDINGS ARE ALL A MEASURE OF HOW YOU CONTINUE TO REINFORCE YOUR SELF IMAGE.

- WHAT IS ALREADY IN YOUR LIFE IS EXACTLY WHAT YOU HAVE ALREADY CREATED UP TO THIS POINT.

Do any of these points resonate with you? Read them and see which describes something about the way you experience your life and write about it in the insight box. In this activity try to give yourself a couple of examples that you can describe in more detail. One example from Jack was he thought that spending every weekend with his two sons, playing tennis, football and other activities, therefore relieving his wife, was what helped him feel good about himself.

His self-confessed arguments with his sons during these weekends seemed to indicate something different however, that something else was behind his actions.

Motivation cannot be driven by someone else's desires or needs. Motivation comes from actions and activities arising from within the individual. After going a little deeper into his actions Jack discovered that he committed every weekend to his children because he wanted to gain respect from his own peers, who he sometimes played golf with at weekends. He wanted to be seen as a great dad by them, the kind of dad he never had. Jack got a sense of superiority because he believed he was a model dad. However, neglecting his desires only created resentment which transformed into criticism towards the achievements of both of his sons in the games they played.

Jack's weekends turned into 'empty robotic and angry' periods that served neither father or sons. Looking at what might really help him to feel good about himself and what he needed to create would deepen his own knowledge and help everyone around him.

Maureen is another interesting case study. She came to weekly 'Creating Game' work shops and could not find the time to be quiet and go within herself on a consistent regular basis, even for a couple of minutes a day. After a few weeks she came rushing into the workshop, exasperated and annoyed and said 'I keep snapping at my husband and kids all the time, why do I feel so angry?' This was a great question, one that many people ask. Frustration and anger arise because we neglect ourselves and our desires and this stands in the way of creating a positive sense of self.

## Focus Point

Close your eyes and take three long deep breaths and blow out the air as you exhale. Why did you decide to play The Creating Game, what was it that made you buy this book? What did the book say to you? Focus on what this means to you.

For example Sally was given the book by a friend and thought 'WOW that's for me'. I asked her what that meant and how did she feel? What did her body tell her? How excited did 'WOW' feel? As Sally began to describe what it had meant to her she became excited and laughed. It is this feeling of being energised and eager, this 'focus point' that you need to keep reminding yourself about as you go through the activities. When you get to the place of feeling your 'focus point', say out loud what it is you feel and want. In Sally's case she burst out with, 'YEAH - I want to have a GREAT life'. You do not need to be specific, detailed, precise or proper about this. Just say how you felt or what motivated you and say it so that your body hears and remembers that excited feeling.

This will spur your intention to succeed forward, providing you with energy at times when you may need it.

# INSIGHT (WHAT INSPIRED YOU TO BUY THIS BOOK? WHAT POINTS RESONATE? )

# It's Already Waiting

Everything you have always ever wanted is at your finger tips, according to the vast majority of self made creators including Wayne Dwyer, Debbie Ford, Edwene Gains, Deepak Chopra, Marianne Williamson and Neale Donald Walsch, some of the great spiritual leaders of our time. They all say the same thing; the world is abundant and just waiting for you to ask for whatever it is that you want.

There are reams of information that describe the Laws of Attraction and the most important ones which will help you to play 'The Creating Game' are these:

- WHATEVER YOU ASK FOR YOU WILL GET

- THOUGHTS CREATE THINGS

- YOU ARE WHAT YOU THINK YOU ARE

- THERE IS ENOUGH FOR EVERYONE

- YOU CREATE EVERYTHING ALREADY

Simple really, but true! So simple, that you often create the problem because it feels too simple and therefore not real and therefore not possible and therefore you won't even try. It can be a vicious circle.

The great news is that it doesn't matter if you don't believe it yet because the Laws of Attraction are not selective – as long as you carry out the activities in this book you will become a conscious creator.

You need to know that joy, happiness; contentment and peace are lifelong states that are brought about by the practice of conscious creating and playing The Creating Game. These states are always ready and waiting inside you to emerge.

You also need to know that the creating of 'tangible things' in your life and the building of momentum with each success is the key to your self esteem, self worth, self awareness and self contentment. It is not the tangible things in themselves, or the places that you choose to go to, nor is it the actual desires that create your joy, happiness, peace or contentment. It is by choosing to create purposefully that we bring about increased awareness and self knowledge.

It is by succeeding in the process of creation that you build more strength to continue creating. Most people do not accept this readily and they find difficulty in letting go of the products of supposed happiness, but a short amount of time spent looking at all your possessions and how long they kept you happy will give you a clue. A new car is always replaced by a newer car, and although we can have fun with our new possessions the speed in which we buy, claim, and own these things is shallow and unrewarding. By working through The Creating Game you begin to sort the wheat from the chaff. The concept of ever more possessions becomes less important; to be replaced by revised ideas about what constitutes happiness. If at the end of the process you are lead to particular situations and physical or material conditions as a pre-requisite for happiness, then you will have eliminated false ideas to be left with the genuine, meaningful ones for you.

The Law of Attraction tells you that whatever you want is already there. It's already available and waiting with your name on it. The problem is we are so consumed with materialism that we hardly know what we really want, or what is our hearts desire.

Once you do know what you want, you simply have to choose. This is a tough concept. In truth, you do not really know what it is that you want. And often if you do have an idea it is not a clear one.

### The key to creating is clarity

The key to creating is to make your request clear and tangible and without ambiguity, to set in motion the energy within you that is part of the universal energy that holds the possibilities of all creation.

## Focus Point

Close your eyes and take three, deep slow breaths and try to imagine what it would REALLY be like to be able to have EVERYTHING that you have ever wanted. That it is all just waiting for you, right here and now. Really see if you can touch that 'focus point' and feel how fantastic that could be.

Imagine just for a moment ...!

Let your heart beat a little faster, let your energy lift a little and then in an action or words make an expression of what it would feel like to have it all!

INSIGHT (HOW DO YOU FEEL)

# Myths About You

You are not what you think you are. Your beliefs are based upon years of continued behaviour patterns that reinforce your negative internal beliefs. The question is "Why are you not creating already, what is it that stops you?"

Society and the quality of life for most individuals is plagued by obstacles that are not real but seem real to most people at any given time. The list below is not exhaustive and there will be particular myths that you use to prevent yourself from creating what you desire. Go through this list and see if any of them describe how you see yourself and give examples of why you believe this is so. Firstly write down which ones you believe are about yourself. Then, before you do any inner voice work take a deep breath and ask your logical brain to help you to see how the myths you carry are simply not based on reality, even though they may feel real for some of the time. Take 'I am too old' and look at this logically. You will undoubtedly know or have read about many people who are older than you, often a great deal older, who have started to create amazing things in their later years. It is not true that anyone can be too old to create. Look at 'I am not nice enough' and again you will be able to bring into your awareness someone or several people who you would consider 'not nice'. This feeling is usually caused by how they behave and not 'who they are'. Regardless of what you think about them, they are still able to create for themselves. It is important to go through the myths and take them apart with your conscious mind. Remember, The Creating Game works no matter what myth you carry about with you.

- I AM NOT GOOD ENOUGH
- I AM STUPID
- I AM TOO OLD
- I AM YOUNG
- I AM A WOMAN
- I AM TOO FAT – TOO THIN
- I AM NOT BEAUTIFUL
- I DON'T DESERVE IT

- I DESERVE TO BE PUNISHED
- I DON'T LOVE MYSELF
- I AM SECOND BEST
- I AM NOT LOVABLE
- I AM TOO POOR
- I AM TOO WEALTHY
- I AM NOT SPIRITUAL ENOUGH
- I AM NOT NICE ENOUGH

Find a comfortable place and see how powerfully you play along with the myths. Choose the statements from this list or from others that you have added which you continue to act out and that stand in your way. Write them down, giving reasons why you continue with each myth. Are you playing out your myths all the time? Is this the excuse you give each time you don't go forward?

**Grade yourself on a scale from one to ten on how
much you perpetuate your myths.**

As an example, I have a friend who constantly says that she is too old to do almost anything, from going to a party to having a discussion. This myth is part of her daily conversation and each day she reinforces that she is old and unable. This puts her at a ten on the scale as she continues to maintain her own myth about being too old. Use this as a benchmark for your own grading; if you find you are constantly reinforcing a myth through thoughts or actions, it should be graded high.

Notice how you see yourself within your myths. Notice whether you are aware of deep habitual ones and chose the strongest ones to work with. Do an EFT sequence on your myth (see Appendix) and release its hold over you by saying 'even though I deserve to be punished, I love and accept myself completely'. Then take a deep breath and move on.

## Focus Point

Close your eyes and take three, deep slow breaths. Now imagine yourself at a party or gathering and everyone is having a wonderful, happy time. You are there amongst the guests and the centre of attention; everyone is listening to you, admiring you, smiling at you. Experience the freedom of having no problems being with people and feeling loved and appreciated. Create a big open smile on your face and allow your whole body to experience it.

INSIGHT ( MYTHS ABOUT YOU )

# Myths About What You Need

Here we look at what you think you need to do or be in order to create. You have constructed some great excuses that stop you from creating on all levels, physical, spiritual and emotional. These can be altered, and this is where we start.

You are not your possessions, your holidays, or whatever the media or anyone else says you are. Possessions and all the holidays and activities in the world cannot create happiness. Happiness and joy are states of mind that come as a result of feeling good about you. Material possessions satisfy cravings for a brief while and then the cravings reassert themselves and you are off on the merry go round again, buying and doing things to quieten the need that gnaws away inside.

You have to be focussed on your creation. You cannot have self-made obstacles in the way that stop you from creating. It is very important that you see this and recognise the things you put in your own way every time you intend to start creating.

To create what you want you do not need to –

- READ ANOTHER BOOK
- BECOME ENLIGHTENED
- GO TO ANOTHER SEMINAR
- FIND ANOTHER GURU
- GO TO CHURCH
- RENOUNCE YOUR SINS
- PRAY ON YOUR KNEES

- HAVE A PARTNER
- HAVE MORE MONEY
- BELIEVE YOU CAN
- BE RIGHT OR WRONG
- BE BAD
- BE GOOD
- GO BACK TO COLLEGE

You need none of these things. They are simply excuses that lead to procrastination and, ultimately, failure. What you do need is clarity about your intention, so let's take a step towards that now.

**Close your eyes and consider where you have made barriers that you believe stop you from creating what you want.**

Connect with your inner voice and look at the excuses you make that continue to hold you back. Don't turn this into a struggle, simply listen to what comes and make a note, then go inside again until you have all the excuses out in the open. Have faith in the truth of your inner voice. Notice how the myths about you and the myths about what you need may be inter linked. You can do an EFT sequence and combine the linked myths saying, 'even though I am stupid and need to go to college, I love and accept myself completely'

Susan was a client who could see that every time she signed up to do another course at college her myth about herself and what she needed were linked together. She could not create what she wanted because she needed to go to college and continue to learn new skills because she was not clever enough. This self perpetuating myth will continue until she examines the reasons behind the need to keep doing more courses. She saw that her combined myths stopped her from taking the leap into creating her own business, something she wanted to do. One of the keys to unlocking 'closed doors' is awareness about the myths we create in our lives.

At this stage of The Creating Game you do not need anything other than a desire and willingness to begin. Later on you will be clarifying what it is you want to create and looking at the steps and resources that will help you to succeed.

## Focus Point

Close your eyes and take three, deep slow breaths. See yourself as a complete and whole person. Do this by imagining a golden light that surrounds your complete body. Let the sense of this light glow and feel it as a dynamic force that will enable you to expand and create everything you desire. This golden light flows through all obstacles and limiting beliefs. Simply enjoy creating this experience.

INSIGHT ( MYTHS ABOUT WHAT YOU NEED )

# Evaluating Yourself

The most effective way to create is to have clarity and to show a great degree of honesty and integrity towards yourself. Sometimes this can be difficult, as you often cannot see yourself as others can. This should not prevent you from making the first step and you could ask a friend to help you if you want to.

Take some time to evaluate yourself right now, read through the following list and answer each question by making a few notes.

| | |
|---|---|
| 1. | DO YOU HAVE CONTROL OF YOUR LIFE? |
| 2. | ARE YOU AWARE OF YOUR THINKING PROCESS? |
| 3. | HOW OFTEN DO YOU GIVE YOURSELF TIME TO JUST SIT AND THINK? |
| 4. | WHAT IS THE MAIN FOCUS OF YOUR THOUGHTS? |
| 5. | WHAT IS IT THAT IS MOST ON YOUR MIND? |
| 6. | HOW OFTEN DO YOU CONSIDER ENVIRONMENTAL ISSUES? |
| 7. | HOW SPIRITUAL ARE YOU? |
| 8. | DO YOU BELIEVE IN GOD? |
| 9. | WHAT DO YOU BELIEVE IN? |
| 10. | DO YOU CARE ABOUT YOUR BODY? |
| 11. | HOW DO YOU CARE FOR YOUR BODY? |
| 12. | WHAT ARE YOUR DAILY PRACTICES OF CARE AND ATTENTION? |
| 13. | DO YOU KNOW WHAT YOU WANT? |
| 14. | HOW DO YOU CARE FOR YOUR LIVING ENVIRONMENT? |
| 15. | HOW OFTEN DO YOU EXERCISE? |
| 16. | WHEN DID YOU LAST GO FOR A WALK? |
| 17. | HOW CLUTTERED IS YOUR ENVIRONMENT? |
| 18. | DO YOU KNOW HOW MUCH MONEY YOU HAVE IN YOUR ACCOUNT? |
| 19. | WHAT DO YOU SPEND MOST OF YOUR MONEY ON? |
| 20. | WHAT DO YOU WANT? |
| 21. | WHAT MAKES YOU HAPPY AND FULFILLED? |
| 22. | WHO DO YOU CARE ABOUT? |

After you have finished sit quietly and dwell on your answers to see what comes up for you. What do your answers tell you about yourself? Do they make you feel light, lively, excited, and happy or is there a sense of disappointment or dismay about how your life seems from responding to this list? Write down a short paragraph about how you see yourself from this short evaluation. The following example should help. If necessary write about yourself in the third person to bring in a sense of self-observation. At one of my workshops Joan wrote this about herself as though she were on the outside looking in.

'Joan seems to be all over the place, not knowing what she wants. When I asked her about her body it was clear that she hates it, she does nothing nice to care for herself. Joan is a very lonely and sad lady who doesn't believe in God because he doesn't care about her. She has a job she hates but loves her grand children. For Joan there is not a lot to live for so she just sits at home at night and watches TV'.

From Joan's own words it was clear to her that she has very little self love and was self critical. I asked Joan to re evaluate and write it as though a therapist, counsellor or caring teacher would see her qualities. This is what she wrote:

'Joan has great difficulty about what she wants from life, but she has great potential. She is a capable, strong and sensitive woman, who is insecure and afraid to communicate her real feelings. So she appears to be angry at the world and God. Joan is a warm and loving grandmother who really wants to make a difference in her community'

Work with your own evaluation and be aware of how you portray yourself through your statement. Check to see how your initial comments might be critical or damning, and see how these negative thoughts have been running away under the surface for years. Also look at how you think others see you and what effect this has on you. Write down how you feel about it at this moment.

## Focus Point

Close your eyes and take three, deep slow breaths. Choose a particular sensitive point from above and visualize this area of your life as being completely perfect, resolved, organised and free of any anxiety.

What ever your evaluation of yourself has shown you that may be negative, see it now as positive and exactly how you would want it to be. Make a deep sigh of certainty knowing that you create everything

## INSIGHT ( MY STATEMENT ABOUT ME )

## EVALUATING YOURSELF

ANSWER EACH QUESTION ON P.19 WITH YOUR PERSONAL NOTES

1. _____
2. _____
3. _____
4. _____
5. _____
6. _____
7. _____
8. _____
9. _____
10. _____
11. _____
12. _____
13. _____
14. _____
15. _____
16. _____
17. _____
18. _____
19. _____
20. _____
21. _____
22. _____

# Your Physical Body

Truly effective creating is achieved by being aware of all aspects of yourself including your physical self. How healthy do you think you are? What do you do to take care of your body? Go through the list and add any other health concerns that you personally have.

Many people are aware that they are over weight but rarely take note of whether their hair shines and their skin is glowing. How do you feel about your health? What does it tell you about your sense of self worth? Is this an area in your life that you regularly neglect, or are you affected by external events? Respond to these points and make notes in the insight box to show where you are not considering your health.

- ARE YOU THE WEIGHT THAT YOU WOULD LIKE TO BE?
- IS YOUR SKIN CLEAR AND GLOWING?
- DOES YOUR HAIR SHINE AND LOOK HEALTHY
- ARE YOUR TEETH WHITE AND STRONG?
- IS YOUR BODY FIRM, LEAN, STRONG AND SUPPLE?
- DO YOU HAVE A FRESH BODY ODOUR?
- ARE YOUR NAILS STRONG AND PLIABLE?
- ARE YOUR EYES BRIGHT?
- ARE YOU PRONE TO ILLNESS?
- DO YOU HAVE HEADACHES?
- DO YOU HAVE ANY SPECIFIC DISEASE?
- HOW WELL DOES YOUR BODY FEEL?
- DO YOU HAVE ACHES AND PAINS?
- DO YOU SUFFER FROM A SPECIFIC ACHE?
- DO YOU HAVE ANY SKIN COMPLAINTS?
- WHAT IS YOUR SLEEP PATTERN LIKE?
- DO YOU EAT HEALTHY FOOD?
- DO YOU SUFFER FROM PALPITATIONS?
- HAVE YOU GOT AN EATING DISORDER?

Now choose the area that causes you the most concern and use EFT: 'Even though I have insomnia, I love and accept myself completely' You may choose to say 'even though I do not care enough about my health I love and accept myself completely'. Later on you may decide to do your creating in an area of health.

## Focus Point

Close your eyes and take three, deep slow breaths. See yourself as a beautiful, healthy, shining being. You are full of vitality, strength and inner joy. Really feel you body as you do this inner work and accept the pleasure that you body feels from this experience. Regardless of your physical state allow yourself to feel radiantly healthy from the inside out.

INSIGHT ( YOUR PHYSICAL BODY )

*"I finally realized that being grateful to my body was key to giving more love to myself."*

## Oprah Winfrey

# Your Behaviour and Why and Why Again

Your behaviour is an important aspect of how you are able to create, what you react to and what triggers your reactions. From the following list answer each question and go deeper into the reality behind each response by asking yourself 'why'. Make a new response, and then ask yourself 'why' again. Here is an example of what you need to do –

**Q. What is it that makes you angry?**

'People who don't listen to me when I talk to them'.

> **Why?** 'Because it's polite to listen'.

> > **Why?** 'Because it's infuriating'.

> > > **Why?** 'I feel like they don't care about me'.

Follow through with each point and simply acknowledge where it leads you.

1.   WHAT IS IT THAT MAKES YOU FEEL DISAPPOINTED IN YOURSELF?

2.   WHO DO YOU BLAME WHEN THINGS GO WRONG?

3.   WHAT IS IT THAT IRRITATES YOU ENOUGH TO CRITICISE?

4.   WHAT ARE YOU PROUD OF ACHIEVING?

5.   WHAT THINGS MAKE YOU FEEL PROUD?

6.   HOW DO YOU GET EXCITED?

7.   WHAT ARE YOU FRUSTRATED WITH?

8.   WHAT DO YOU REALLY WANT?

9.   WHAT IS IT THAT MAKES YOU CRY?

10.  WHO IS IT THAT MAKES YOU ANGRY?

11.  WHAT ARE YOU ASHAMED OF?

12.  WHAT WOULD YOU CHANGE IF YOU COULD?

13.  HOW DO YOU STAND UP FOR YOURSELF?

14.  HOW DO YOU MAKE YOUR SELF HEARD?

15.  WHAT TYPE OF PERSON INFURIATES YOU?

16.  WHAT INCIDENTS MAKE YOUR BLOOD BOIL?

Continued...

17.  WHAT DISTRESSES YOU?

18.  WHAT DO YOU DO TO FIND RELIEF?

19.  WHAT DO YOU DO TO MAKE YOURSELF FEEL BETTER?

20.  WHAT ARE YOUR COMFORT BLANKETS?

21.  WHAT MAKES YOU LAUGH?

22.  WHO MAKES YOU LAUGH?

23.  WHO DO YOU GO TO TALK ABOUT YOUR TROUBLES?

When you feel you are being lead on a journey of discovery take time to connect with your inner voice and your solar plexus chakra. When you react to what comes up, place your hand on your belly button area, the region of your solar plexus chakra (see Appendix). Take deep breaths and swell out your belly and feel any inner angst that may be there.

Many people have stomach problems that they call 'that sinking feeling' which stems from tension and stress. These feelings lodge in the solar plexus chakra. Breathe gently and evenly into your belly and imagine a soft, calm, candle flame inside your solar plexus. See if you can imagine it gently swaying providing inner light and soothing warmth.

Choose any points that affected you from simply reading some of the questions. Check to see the impact they made. There might be a reason for you to do some EFT work with these sensitive areas that affect your behaviour towards yourself and others. Follow the EFT guidelines in the Appendix and say your set up statement. For example:

'Even though I couldn't stand up for myself as a little girl, I love and accept myself completely'

You should take a rest after this activity as it can be an emotional experience. Stop for a while, drink some water and reflect on how your awareness is evolving. Write down how you feel about this particular exercise. What does it tell you about your behaviour patterns?

## Focus Point

Close your eyes and take three, deep slow breaths. Imagine yourself acting out any of the behaviour problems that you see in yourself. See yourself as a small child who needs to be accepted and forgiven for this behaviour and soften your inner self, by taking some extra slow breaths and letting your body relax. Smile and acknowledge that all is well in the world.

## INSIGHT ( MY STATEMENT ABOUT ME )

## EVALUATING YOURSELF

ANSWER EACH QUESTION ON P.25 - 26 WITH YOUR PERSONAL NOTES

1. _____
2. _____
3. _____
4. _____
5. _____
6. _____
7. _____
8. _____
9. _____
10. _____
11. _____
12. _____
13. _____
14. _____
15. _____
16. _____
17. _____
18. _____
19. _____
20. _____
21. _____
22. _____
23. _____

*"All things belong to us; that is, all things are ready for us whenever we can use them; but we can not use the greater things in life so long as we are living a small, partially dormant life. The riches of the kingdom are not for us 'to have and to hold;' they are for us to use; and we can use them all only as we become alive with the life more abundant in every element of body, mind and soul."*

Christian D. Larson

# Emotional You

This exercise helps you to realise what is going on inside your emotional self and how you feel when your emotions are triggered. It helps you discover what happens to your body and what you think and say to yourself when your emotions take over. Notice the difference between this exercise and the last one. This exercise helps you to see how emotional reactions show up in your body or your behaviour.

Answer all the questions, paying attention to how and where your emotions show up in your body and how your mind interprets them. Your awareness of these feelings may surprise you.

1.    HOW DO YOU KNOW WHEN YOU ARE HAPPY, HOW DOES YOUR BODY FEEL, AND WHAT ARE YOU THINKING?

2.    WHAT DO YOU DO WHEN YOU FEEL TENSE, WHICH AREA IN YOUR BODY DO YOU FEEL IT?

3.    WHEN SOMEONE UPSETS YOU WHAT DO YOU FEEL?

4.    WHEN YOU ARE UPSET, WHERE IN YOUR BODY DO YOU REACT AND WHAT DO YOU SAY TO YOURSELF ?

5.    IF YOU ARE LET DOWN BY A LOVED ONE WHAT DOES THIS MEAN TO YOU?

6.    WHEN YOU MEET SOMEONE YOU DON'T LIKE WHAT GOES ON IN YOUR HEAD AND DO YOU HAVE A REACTION IN YOUR BODY?

7.    WHAT IS IT THAT MAKES YOU DISTRUSTFUL OF SOMEONE, HOW DO YOU KNOW THAT YOU ARE FEELING THIS, WHAT HAPPENS IN YOUR HEAD AND BODY?

8.    WHY DO YOU GET DEFENSIVE, WHAT ARE YOU DEFENDING, DO YOU CRY OR FEEL ANGRY?

9.    WHAT IS IT THAT MAKES YOU REBELLIOUS, WHAT ARE YOU REBELLING AGAINST?

10.   WHAT IS IT THAT STOPS YOU FROM BEING CO-OPERATIVE, WHAT HAPPENS WHEN YOU ARE UN-COOPERATIVE IN YOUR BODY AND MIND?

11.   WHAT THINGS CAN YOU NOT FORGIVE AND WHY, WHERE DO YOU FEEL THIS IN YOUR BODY?

12.   WHAT IS IT THAT MAKES YOU FEEL AS THOUGH YOUR HEART IS BREAKING?

13.   WHAT MAKES YOUR HEART SING, HOW DOES THIS FEEL IN YOUR BODY AND MIND?

14.   WHO AND WHAT KIND OF PERSON MAKES YOUR HEART SING?

15.   WHY DO YOU TELL LIES AND WHAT DOES IT FEEL LIKE IN YOUR BODY TO TELL LIES?

Continued...

16. WHAT MAKES YOU FEEL SADNESS AND WHERE DO YOU FEEL IT IN YOUR BODY?

17. WHAT MAKES YOU GOSSIP ABOUT OTHERS AND HOW DOES IT FEEL TO GOSSIP?

18. WHAT MAKES YOU JUDGE OTHERS AND HOW DO YOU FEEL WHEN YOU JUDGE SOMEONE?

If a specific point makes an impact on you, do an EFT sequence on that area and release the emotions that are stuck in your cellular structure.

All the exercises in The Creating Game help you become aware and alert about the creating you have engaged in throughout your life. Having clarity on how you have created in the past and the limiting life patterns that have stopped you from being conscious creators will help you manifest what you desire through conscious awareness.

As you work through these exercises you will begin to see how in certain areas you repeat the same thing again and again. You will recognise it as it surfaces and you will then have a choice to see it for what it really is, usually as a limiting belief. You can then acknowledge it, choose to use EFT on the problem if you wish and then move on.

## Focus Point

Close your eyes and take three, deep slow breaths. Place your hand on your heart chakra and imagine a soft rose pink light of compassion surrounding your heart area. Imagine your heart feeling softer, warmer, and calmer and filling with compassionate feelings.

Accept these feelings of self love and forgive yourself for anything that hurts you. You can come back to this focus again and again; it will help you to release any guilt or grief that you may carry in your heart.

INSIGHT ( HOW DO I FEEL? )

## EVALUATING EMOTIONS

ANSWER EACH QUESTION ON P.29 - 30 WITH YOUR PERSONAL NOTES

1. _____
2. _____
3. _____
4. _____
5. _____
6. _____
7. _____
8. _____
9. _____
10. _____
11. _____
12. _____
13. _____
14. _____
15. _____
16. _____
17. _____
18. _____

# Looking at the Past

At this point in The Creating Game we need to take a short stroll into our past. This can often be a difficult proposition because what we remember is usually seen through the eyes of the child we used to be. It is rare when you look back that you will be able to have a real picture of the truth. Children see things quite differently than adults and they believe most of what an adult says to them, particularly their parents.

Children hear and see things from a different perspective and this perspective does not shift easily when you become an adult. You would not be affected by the same situation you experienced as a child if the very same event happened today, and yet those earlier impressions persist within our emotional framework, colouring the present day. What affects you is the way you feel about certain events that remind the small child that still exists within you of the pain you experienced as that child.

A simple example might be that as a six year old child your parents caught you exploring your genitals in the bath, something that is perfectly natural, but which, because of your parents upbringing they saw as something shameful. You were scolded or smacked or both and you also experienced your parents own deep shame at that moment. This incident had a profound effect on you and because it causes discomfort and pain to think about it you bury the actual incident. But what keeps coming back is the way you felt when it happened. When some one touches the memory of this event by speaking in the same tone of voice as your parent, or uses similar words to those your parents used in a situation that might involve intimacy or nakedness you will relive many of the emotions that you felt as a six year old child.

Often you do not know where the depth of this emotion springs from and at a later time you are often surprised and perplexed at what happened. The triggers for these past events can be incredibly small and appear insignificant. If you were to tell someone about it, unless they too had a similar childhood experience they would find your deep reaction out of proportion to what had been said. However, their own childhood has its own 'demons' based upon their different experiences and incidents. When you prepare yourself and spend time reliving some of the incidents from your past you are able to get a more adult perspective on the reality of what that holds for you today. You can begin to understand that your own parents had their own 'demons' to deal with, that their parents had their own and so on. Your job is to break the chain for you and your own children. This is not an exercise in dredging up the past: it is a mature look at your childhood and a way of taking a different perspective on any hurtful events that you may have experienced.

**In this exercise begin by going directly to the focus point at the end of this chapter and following the instructions.**

Then read the following list and notice which ones make an impact on you and resonates with how you feel about your past.

---

- YOU MAY HAVE EXPERIENCED CRITICISM AND CONDEMNATION, FROM PARENTS, OLDER FAMILY MEMBERS AND TEACHERS, TO AN EXTENT THAT THERE IS A SENSE YOU CAN NEVER DO ANYTHING RIGHT.

- YOU MAY FEEL THAT YOU HAD NOT BEEN UNDERSTOOD BY LOVED ONES; YOU MAY HAVE FELT INVISIBLE AND BEEN TOLD TO GO AWAY, OR THAT CHILDREN SHOULD BE SEEN AND NOT HEARD. THIS IS A COMMON THEME WITH MANY FAMILIES. WRITE DOWN ANY SIGNIFICANT TIMES THAT YOUR FEELINGS, NEEDS AND CHILDHOOD DESIRES WERE NOT HEARD. THERE WILL HAVE BEEN TIMES WHEN YOU NEEDED ADVICE, OR A LOVING SHOULDER TO CRY ON AND HAD NOWHERE TO GO. IT'S IMPORTANT TO GIVE SPECIFIC EXAMPLES.

- DID YOU FEEL YOU HAD TO LIVE UP TO A BROTHER OR SISTER, BEEN MADE TO FEEL THAT YOU ARE NOT AS GOOD AS, CLEVER AS, PRETTY AS, OR BRAVE AS THEM, OR BEEN COMPARED TO ANOTHER FAMILY MEMBER OR A NEIGHBOUR'S CHILD. WRITE ABOUT HOW YOU FELT EVERY TIME YOU WERE COMPARED AND WHAT YOU HAVE MADE THIS MEAN TO YOU IN ADULT LIFE.

- YOU MAY HAVE HAD TO BE OR DO SOMETHING THAT YOU DID NOT WANT TO, SO THAT YOUR PARENTS COULD BOOST THEIR OWN SELF ESTEEM. MANY CHILD STARS HAVE A DEEP SENSE OF INADEQUACY BECAUSE THEY ARE LIVING THEIR PARENT'S DREAMS AND NOT THEIR OWN.

- YOU MAY HAVE BEEN FORCED TO DO THINGS THAT WERE BEYOND YOUR CAPABILITIES BECAUSE OF YOUR AGE, WHICH CAN CAUSE A LACK OF SELF WORTH AND A NEED TO BE PERFECT. THIS CAN HAPPEN WHEN CHILDREN ARE FORCED INTO POTTY TRAINING BEFORE THEY ARE READY OR CAPABLE OF UNDERSTANDING COMPLEX BEHAVIOUR BEFORE THEY ARE PHYSICALLY OR EMOTIONALLY DEVELOPED.

- YOU MAY HAVE BEEN BLAMED OR FELT BLAME FOR WHAT HAPPENED AS A CHILD. MANY CHILDREN BELIEVE IT IS THEIR FAULT THAT THEIR PARENTS DIVORCE OFTEN BECAUSE THE CHILD IS SENT AWAY OR REMOVED FROM THE ARGUMENTS TO ANOTHER ROOM, GIVING AN IMPRESSION OF BLAME.

- YOU MAY HAVE EXPERIENCED TEASING, CRITICISM OR BULLYING BECAUSE YOUR APPEARANCE DOESN'T CONFORM TO YOUR PARENTS, SIBLINGS OR SOCIETY'S NORM. MANY CHILDREN SUFFER FROM 'IMAGE' INADEQUACIES WHICH CARRY ON TO ADULT LIFE." I AM NOT PRETTY OR HANDSOME ENOUGH".

- WERE YOU BROUGHT UP ON REWARD AND PUNISHMENT? YOU WILL GET SOMETHING IF YOU ARE GOOD AND BE PUNISHED IF YOU ARE BAD, RATHER THAN BEING ENCOURAGED TO UNDERSTAND YOUR MISTAKES AND LEARN AND REALISE THE CONSEQUENCES OF WRONG BEHAVIOUR.

- YOU HAVE ISSUES AROUND SOCIAL, CULTURAL OR ETHNIC UPBRINGING, WHICH HAS AFFECTED YOUR SELF ESTEEM.

Continued...

- YOU HAVE ISSUES AROUND SOCIAL, CULTURAL OR ETHNIC UPBRINGING, WHICH HAS AFFECTED YOUR SELF ESTEEM.

- YOUR PARENTS MAY HAVE FELT THAT IT WAS IMPORTANT IN LIFE TO HAVE MORE, TO KEEP UP WITH THE JONESES, THAT THE MORE YOU HAD THE BETTER YOU WERE. MUCH OF THE WAY CHILDREN VIEW OUR SOCIETY IS BASED ON MATERIALISM. TV AND THE INTERNET ENCOURAGES THE PREMISE THAT MONEY AND POSSESSIONS MAKE US MORE WORTHY. MANY MILLIONAIRES CAN TELL YOU THAT THIS IS NOT TRUE; THEY ALSO HAVE FEELINGS OF LONELINESS, LACK OF SELF WORTH AND DEPRESSION.

---

This list is an example of possible past childhood experiences; you may have other more specific examples like sexual abuse, alcoholism or divorce. Write down your own examples and ask, 'How does it feel. What do I say about myself when I recall what happened'. Read through every one and write down any significant times, situations and events you can recall that correspond with these points. Notice how it feels to read about the things that happened in your past and how these have helped to shape you and your behaviour today. Note that these are common experiences for many children and that many continue to feel the impact of them into their adult lives. Notice this is a general list and not a special list: many children go through the same experiences. It does not make you special to have these experiences and make notes on how it feels to know that you're not alone in this.

Notice whether you feel that you want to keep hold of these experiences because they help you to remain a victim. Simply observe what happens when you do this whole exercise. Choose which ones have the greatest impact and score them one to ten, ten being the most intense and do a round of EFT basic recipe. Make notes of how you feel after EFT.

## Focus Point

Close your eyes and take three, deep slow breaths. Imagine yourself as a small child in any of the situations above and see what it now feels like for you.

Do you still feel the tension, hurt, sadness or anger? Breathe deeply feeling any sensations and imagine yourself as an adult and with mature experience and understanding. How would you respond to this experience now, what would you say? How would you stick up for yourself? Who would you tell about it? Let yourself respond in an appropriate manner so that you can feel the sensation of being more in control. Acknowledge that these things are in the past and it is not necessary to continue to hold on to them, having them influence your life.

Notice how you feel when you empower your child of the past and write about your experience doing this exercise.

# INSIGHT ( LOOKING AT THE PAST )

# Being the Victim

Being the victim means you do not need to take responsibility for yourself, your behaviour or your actions. Being the victim means you are the one that is hurting and something or someone is to blame for how you see yourself. In my workshops many people understand this concept and yet are still unwilling to take responsibility for how they feel, behave or act and sometimes they are unable to react in any other way than as a victim. We all fall into this trap. Attention to your own awareness is the key to understanding your victim behaviour. Only you can discover why you choose to remain a victim and what it is you will need to give up to stop being a victim.

In one of my workshops I worked with Eric, who had been ill for a long time. He talked about how ill he was and what it stopped him from doing. On the basis of searching for his particular victim behaviour I decided to turn his understanding of the situation around and asked him what it was that being ill enabled him to do. He was shocked at the prospect that he could be getting something out of being ill. He went through the activities and could soon see he got lots of attention from caring ladies when he was ill, far more than he had ever got as a well man. He also didn't have to go to work every day, he could spend time writing his book and receive sickness benefit. After realising he had a lot of things invested in his illness I asked him if he was willing to give up his illness and he said no. At lunchtime he thanked me and excused himself from the class. He had made a new choice one that was in integrity with his real desire, to be unwell.

Let's look at what you do to perpetuate your victim state.

- WHEN YOU ARE PLAYING A VICTIM, YOU ARE NEVER CREATING. BEING UNWILLING TO LOOK AT YOUR DESIRES, CREATE YOUR LIFE AND HAVE A PURPOSE TO FOLLOW PERPETUATES VICTIM HOOD. PLAYING THE CREATING GAME WILL CHANGE YOUR BELIEF IN YOURSELF AND MOVE YOU FROM BEING THE VICTIM THAT BLAMES TO A PERSON WHO CREATES.

- YOU DO NOT SEPARATE YOURSELF FROM WHAT YOU DO. THERE MAY HAVE BEEN A TIME WHEN YOU HAVE BEHAVED BADLY; AN EXAMPLE MIGHT BE THAT YOU WERE UNFAITHFUL IN YOUR MARRIAGE. YOU CHOOSE TO CONTINUE BEING GUILTY, CARRYING YOUR SHAME AND CONNECTING THIS WITH YOUR SELF WORTH RATHER THAN DO SOMETHING ABOUT IT. BEING WILLING TO SEPARATE FROM YOUR ACTIONS, LEARN FROM THEM AND ACCEPT THEM FOR THE MISTAKES THEY ARE TAKES YOU FROM BEING A VICTIM TO A POSITION OF STRENGTH AND RESPONSIBILITY.

- AS A VICTIM YOU DO NOT TAKE RESPONSIBILITY FOR YOUR LIFE, YOU DEPEND ON OTHERS TO PROVIDE YOU WITH THE THINGS YOU ARE NOT WILLING TO DO FOR YOURSELF.

Continued...

- YOU CONTINUE BEING A VICTIM BECAUSE YOU DO NOT BELIEVE THAT EVERYTHING YOU NEED IS ALREADY AVAILABLE WITHIN THIS UNIVERSE WE LIVE IN. YOU DO NOT HAVE FAITH IN WHAT IS POSSIBLE; SOMEHOW YOU ARE THE VICTIM THAT CANNOT HAVE ACCESS TO UNIVERSAL ENERGY BECAUSE YOU ARE NOT WORTHY.

- AS A VICTIM YOU TAKE THE EASIEST OPTION RATHER THAN MAKING THE EFFORT TO WORK AT CREATING SOMETHING DIFFERENT. YOU SAY IT'S TOO HARD AND YOUR UNWILLINGNESS TO STICK TO WHAT YOU CLAIM YOU WANT AND CONTINUE INSTEAD TO INDULGE IN YOUR HABITS KEEPS YOU A VICTIM.

- AS A VICTIM YOU BELIEVE THAT YOU NEED PERMISSION TO GO FORWARD AND CREATE WHAT YOU DESIRE. MANY WOMEN HAVE THIS VICTIM STATUS, SAYING 'I WILL HAVE TO ASK MY HUSBAND FIRST!' THIS IS A USEFUL WAY FOR SOME WOMEN TO GIVE THE RESPONSIBILITY TO OTHERS AND THEN BLAME THEM. VICTIMS ARE UNWILLING TO SEE THAT AS ADULTS THEY ARE THEIR OWN AUTHORITY.

- A VICTIM IS UNWILLING TO LEARN HOW TO GO FORWARD IN LIFE AND HAS MANY REASONS; 'I AM TOO OLD', 'TOO YOUNG' OR 'TOO STUPID.'

- YOU STRENGTHEN YOUR VICTIM STATUS BY CONTINUING WITH SELF NEGATING CHATTER. OFTEN YOU DO NOT HEAR IT, BUT IT RUNS LIKE A SOUNDTRACK IN THE BACK OF YOUR CONSCIOUSNESS. AS A VICTIM YOU ARE UNLIKELY TO WANT TO HEAR IT AND WORK TO BE AWARE AND CHANGE IT.

- YOU BELIEVE THAT YOU NEED TO BE PERFECT TO BE OK IN THE WORLD. BEING PERFECT MEANS THAT YOU WILL ALWAYS HAVE TO FAIL AT SOMETHING, BECAUSE YOU CANNOT BE PERFECT ALL OF THE TIME.

- YOU RELY ON OTHERS TO GIVE YOU A SENSE OF SELF WORTH, IMPORTANCE AND VALIDATION. WHEN THINGS GO WRONG OR THAT PERSON LEAVES YOU CAN BLAME THEM FOR CONTROLLING YOUR LIFE OR THE SITUATION.

---

There are many people who play the victim who also believe that the world, God, Mother Earth, the Universe is against them. You hear them say "What will be will be? It's written in the stars. There is nothing I can do to change a thing!". You too will have victim statements that you use to blame the world.

You'll be able to find other ways in which you choose to continue your victim myth. What is it that you hide behind? The following process will help you discover your own excuses.

- TAKE A MOMENT TO SIT UP STRAIGHT WHEREVER YOU MAY BE, THIS WILL SUBLIMINALLY INSTRUCT THE BODY AND MIND TO CONNECT IN THE PARTNERSHIP OF CREATING.

- CLOSE YOUR EYES; TAKE THREE SLOW, DEEP AND EVEN BREATHS.

- LET YOURSELF BE OPEN TO ANY ANSWERS THAT YOU RECEIVE, WITHOUT JUDGEMENT.

- RELAX THE BODY, CHECK SHOULDERS AND FACE FOR TENSION AND TIGHTNESS.

- IMAGINE THAT SOMEONE IS ASKING YOU WHY YOU HAVE NOT BEEN ABLE TO DO SOME THING, OR GO SOMEWHERE, OR HAVE A SPECIFIC THING. MAYBE YOU HAVE BEEN TALKING ABOUT APPLYING FOR A NEW JOB AND AT THE FINAL STAGE OF APPLYING YOU CHANGE YOUR MIND. WHAT REASONS DO YOU GIVE YOUR FRIEND FOR WHY YOU DID NOT GO FORWARD? WHAT WOULD YOU SAY? WHAT EXCUSES WOULD YOU MAKE? IS YOUR RESPONSE 'OH IT JUST WASN'T FOR ME!' OR 'AFTER THINKING ABOUT IT, I DIDN'T REALLY WANT TO WORK THERE!' AND THEN ASK THE QUESTION 'WHY?' YOU CAN DO THIS WITH ALMOST ANYTHING THAT YOU DECIDE TO CHANGE YOUR MIND ABOUT AND YOU CAN DO SELF ENQUIRY WITH YOUR RELATIONSHIP ISSUES. WHY DO YOU STAY IN A DULL OR UNHAPPY RELATIONSHIP?

- LISTEN TO YOUR EXCUSES, YOUR REASONING AND HOW YOU CONTINUE TO PERPETUATE YOUR VICTIM POSITION AND WRITE DOWN WHAT COMES TO YOU. WHAT DOES THIS TELL YOU ABOUT HOW YOU STOP YOURSELF FROM TAKING RESPONSIBILITY FOR YOUR LIFE AND HOW YOU HAVE BEEN CREATING YOUR LIFE UP TO NOW? WHEN YOU CHOOSE TO BE A VICTIM THE PEOPLE AND SITUATIONS THAT YOU ATTRACT WILL BE IN DIRECT ALIGNMENT WITH THIS ROLE THAT YOU PLAY. LOOK AT THE PEOPLE AND SITUATIONS THAT YOU HAVE ALREADY CREATED THAT FIT IN WITH HOW YOU PRESENT YOURSELF AS A VICTIM.

- DO NOT ANALYSE THE ANSWERS OR MAKE THEM FIT WHAT YOU REALLY WANT TO HEAR, SIMPLY MAKE NOTES AND SEE IF YOUR AWARENESS TO HOW YOU ARE CREATING YOUR LIFE IS EXPANDING.

## Focus Point

Close your eyes and take three, deep slow breaths. You will be able to connect to one of the above and will know that you perpetuate your victim status by acting out your patterns.

Imagine yourself in one of the situations where you play out your victim role and watch as clearly as you can how you perform.

Now as you are standing back and looking in on your victim game, exaggerate the performance. Like a Greek tragedy, wail, scream, stamp your feet, throw yourself on the floor, sulk, argue, crouch in a corner and hide. In your visualisation do what ever you do as a victim and really indulge to the point that you are amused at your performance. Try to laugh at yourself!

# INSIGHT ( BEING A VICTIM )

# What Do You Think You Want?

You are going to write down a list of things you think you want. Do not analyse your list in any way. Then write down the reason why you want them. Try not to hold back on the things you want or the reasons you want them. At this stage it is important for you to simply get your desires, ideas and notes out into the open and written into the book in the insight section. As you write your list of 'wants' you may find that the ones you thought of earlier do not seem as significant as you first thought they were. If this happens then just draw a line right through them, but leaving them visible for you to read them.

**Do not hold back.**
**Write down all the things you really want to have in your life.**

The key to creating is to know for certain whether you have got it, that you know you have achieved it. Ask yourself the question 'how will I know that I've got it?' – It is very important to be able to say I have achieved this. Many people ask for things that are global and not tangible like 'peace, contentment or happiness, to be happy'. This is too 'big' to be able to see whether it has happened. This kind of desire is so enormously wide that it will fall by the wayside. These global desires are 'states of being' and although we can continue to work towards feeling peaceful and being happy, we need more specific creations that we can work on through particular activities that enhance our lives.

Without these specific creations what would happen? Would that mean you could never be happy or content ever again? No it does not! It means that you are human and will respond to different situations and events. The benefit of creating is that when you are able to create effectively and consistently you will automatically increase your states of happiness and contentment. Creation gives you energy and power that lead to vastly increased self worth which in turn creates happiness. Although you can desire happiness or any other transititionary state in life, getting it requires life plans that we can consistently play with throughout The Creating Game.

So close your eyes and place your hand on your lower abdomen just below your belly button. This is the area of your creativity, where the sacral chakra lies. This is where you can help to release the energy of creativity *(see chakras in the Appendix).*

Do not worry if you do not believe what you're doing or think it's a bit weird, do it anyway. Place your flat palm on your sacral chakra, close your eyes and take three slow breaths. Swell up your abdomen with your inner breath and let your body be more relaxed. Say out loud three times vam, vam, vam and let the vibration of the sound resonate vvvvvaaaaammmmm, vvvvvvaaaaammmmm, vvvvvvvvvaaaaaaaammmmm, do one final breath and then ask yourself 'What do I really want?'

Just allow anything and everything to pop up and write it down regardless of how wild and wonderful it may be. At one of my creating game workshops Kath came up with a castle in Scotland where she could do holistic medicine, she immediately said 'Oh that's too silly, too much to ask, I will never get that!'

Don't tell yourself that you can't have it, just write it down. Don't be afraid to write down whatever comes, even if you have some negative self talk in the background like Kath did.

Write your full list and be sure to include anything that you think you want. Don't hold back, write down as many desires that you can think of on the facing page. You can keep your list for future creating.

Later on in the book you will choose from this list and clarify your creation in detail. You will only work on one creation through the next three month period. This list can have huge ideas and tiny desires and as you grow in experience you can choose more adventurous ones.

At this stage of your game the intention is to have fun and compile a list that has no restrictions.

**Big or small it does not matter let your ideas flow!**

Now do a scale for each one and grade the desire that you have for each one, number ten being the most desirable and number one being the least desired.

## Focus Point

Close your eyes and take three, deep slow breaths. Imagine yourself having whatever it is that desire. See yourself on a wonderful empty beach, on your own desert island, swimming in a clear blue ocean, driving a racing car, wearing designer clothes, walking down a red carpet, eating at a famous restaurant. Is your desire a new home?

Bring in all your senses and SEE your new home, TOUCH the furniture in your visualisation, SMELL the fresh flowers on the table, LISTEN to the music playing in your lounge, TASTE the sweetness of joy as you wander. Expand yourself and indulge in the desires of your heart and simply enjoy.

- TO GO TO THE CARIBBEAN
- WRITE A BOOK OF POEMS
- DESIGN MY GARDEN
- LEARN TO PLAY GOLF
- HAVE A FABULOUS RELATIONSHIP
- LEARN TO DANCE THE SALSA
- GO FOR A WEEKEND SPA HOLIDAY
- WRITE A BOOK
- BUY A HOUSE IN THE COUNTRY
- ORGANISE A DINNER PARTY FOR 10 PEOPLE
- BREED DOGS
- MEDITATE FOR AN HOUR A DAY
- WRITE MY LIFE STORY
- JOIN A CHOIR
- GO TO THE CINEMA EVERY WEEK
- JOIN A WOMEN'S GROUP
- DECORATE MY LOUNGE
- HAVE MY HAIR COMPLETELY RESTYLED
- WRITE A BOOK OF FAMILY RECIPES
- DESIGN AND COMPLETE A PHOTO ALBUM OF MY FRIENDS
- JOIN A POTTERY CLASS AND MAKE A VASE
- PAINT A WATERCOLOUR PICTURE
- LEARN YOGA
- MAKE A RANGE OF MY OWN HOME MADE JAMS
- DESIGN A SELECTION OF CARDS AND SEND THEM TO ALL MY FRIENDS
- REORGANISE MY HOUSE
- START A NEW BUSINESS
- MAKE A NEW OUTFIT
- WRITE A CHILDREN'S STORY
- LEARN TO SWIM
- GO ON A FOREIGN COOKERY COURSE
- RIDE A HARLEY DAVIDSON BIKE
- CLIMB A MOUNTAIN
- DO A MARATHON
- BECOME A VOLUNTEER
- MAKE A NEW COFFEE TABLE
- MAKE ALL MY CHRISTMAS PRESENTS
- LEARN TO MAKE MY OWN CHOCOLATES
- BUY A RED DRESS AND MATCHING SHOES

# NOW MAKE YOUR LIST ( WHAT DO I THINK I WANT? )

# Why Do You Want It?

Have a break and then go through your list and write down the reasons why you want each thing. Don't spend too much time dwelling on this; take breaths between each one asking 'Why do I want this?' and let your answers unfold. Go through your list and write down all the reasons why you want each one. Notice whether your reasons are similar to the list in 'What makes you feel good and why?'

Check to see if you are still looking to create things for someone else, or to get something for someone else, or if your desire is something to fill a space in your life to make you feel worthy.

Remember that self love comes from within. Nothing that you create will help you to feel more loved; it may get you more partners and more fun at the time, but if it were taken away from you what would happen to your sense of self worth? There is absolutely nothing wrong with having beautiful, exciting fun things and relationships in themselves.

It is the reason behind the desire that makes the difference. You should desire it because you love the concept of it and the creation of it rather than wanting something because your world is empty in that area and you think you need to fill it. You are also not taking something away, you are creating it. If you want to lose weight you must change your statement into one of creating not of losing. For example 'I choose to be a size (?) and be excited about my new body shape'. You should be excited and motivated by the very thought of it .You you must love it enough to manifest it into being. Whether you think you deserve it or not isn't important. What matters is how much you are in love with the idea of bringing it into the world.

When we truly know what we love and desire we are then willing to put in the time to create it. Without persistent desire there is no creation. So go ahead and take a deep breath, follow the simple inner voice guidelines and ask yourself 'Why do I think I want this?' Again there is no need to analyse this in any depth; your awareness is expanding every time you do these exercises, and they will help you to play The Game of Creating faster and more successfully.

## Focus Point

Close your eyes and take three, deep slow breaths and see yourself surrounded by the things on your list. Go from one to another and see how it feels to want each one. Let the ones that feel empty and unexciting fade from the picture. The ones that make your heart jump for joy, touch them, play with them, enjoy them in your mind.

# WHY DO YOU WANT IT?

*"When I dare to be powerful, to use my strength in the service of my vision, then it becomes less and less important whether I am afraid."*

*Audre Lorde*

# Why Haven't You Got It Already?

Now look at your list and go through each one and ask these questions

- WHY HAVEN'T I GOT IT ALREADY?

- WHAT IS STOPPING ME FROM GETTING IT?

- WHAT WILL I HAVE TO DO TO GET IT AND AM I REALLY WILLING TO GO FOR IT?

- WHAT WILL I HAVE TO GIVE UP TO GET IT? THINK ABOUT THIS ONE A MOMENT. WILL YOU HAVE TO GIVE UP HAVING SYMPATHY FROM PEOPLE, WILL YOU HAVE TO GIVE UP BEING CO-DEPENDENT, WILL YOU HAVE TO GIVE UP BEING THE 'STUPID' ONE, AND WILL YOU HAVE TO GIVE UP COMPLAINING?

- DO I REALLY WANT TO CREATE THIS?

- WHAT LIMITING BELIEFS DO YOU HAVE FOR NOT HAVING IT ALREADY?

Now go through the list and see which ones hold the biggest blocks and doubts for you. Which ones say, 'Yeah right, who are you kidding', which desires shout, 'No chance you will never get that!' which ones say 'I am not good enough?' – Check your list for the strongest negative charges and pick the three that you believe are not possible.

Grade yourself on a scale of one to ten, where ten means you are certain it's not possible to get this and one means that it is very likely that you will create it. Note down this number and how you feel regarding your desired creation. If your number was ten and you really do not think you will ever get what you want, how does it feel to see this and admit that even though you want it you actually believe you will never get it? Do you feel sadness, disappointment, anger or something else; write down what you are feeling.

Left alone these emotional obstacles would continue to hold you back. So, whenever we discover them we shift energy to remove them. They present an opportunity to use EFT to clear your energy fields and set up a new situation in which change and success are possible.

In Kath's situation we began her setup statement with 'Even though I do not think I can have a castle in Scotland and feel disappointed, I love and accept myself completely' and so on through the Basic Recipe.

Kath opened herself to new possibilities by removing the blocking inner voice that said she will never get it. She embraced and acknowledged her blocks and negative inner chatter. This allowed the blockage to soften and be less rigid, less certain in its intensity, less self confirming and self sabotaging.

Kath is now more able to allow changes in her life that will lead her to what she truly desires. Instead of stopping the desire in its tracks, she created space to let in the possibilities that were available to her.

Two weeks after Kath's creation work she called me to tell me her husband had begun to build her a studio as an extension to their home. She was excited and pleased and even more so when she began to explain what it looked like. She said it has stone flags and old pillars and was quite grand looking. I asked her what she thought it reminded her of and she gasped and said 'Oh my goodness it's just like a miniature castle'. We laughed and I told her she could have anything she wanted and that her past conditioning about not being able to have what you really want simply needed a little more work, but she was certainly getting there!

When you have finished doing EFT with your main blockages, re-evaluate them and see where you are with your scoring and how far you have moved from your original score Notice how open you feel, how much more relaxed and more positive about what you truly desire. Also notice if after EFT you actually feel like any of your desires have faded away and do not seem so important anymore.

Write down any changes of feeling against your list of desires.

## Focus Point

Close your eyes and take three, slow breaths and breath deeply into your belly, place your hand on your middle and let your belly swell with your breath. Each time you exhale imagine all the problems, limiting beliefs and reasons you have come up with to be blown away with your breath. Do this until you really do feel that you have created some space inside your body and you feel lighter and less burdened.

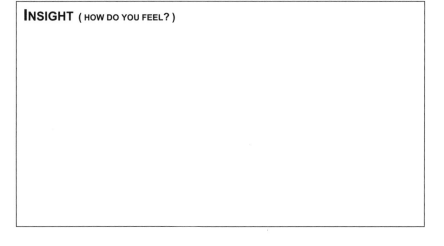

INSIGHT ( HOW DO YOU FEEL? )

48

## WHY HAVEN'T I GOT IT ALREADY?

# Conventional Sabotaging

You have looked at many things that have influenced the way you've been creating your life up to know and the many reasons that hold you back in creating your best life. Let's now look at some of the sabotaging techniques you might begin to bring into your game at this point. Things look like they might change for the better, so why wouldn't you sabotage them? Up to now you have been working on familiar ground, looking at the past, looking at the effect your emotions have had on you and at the other areas that show where you have been unconsciously creating to date.

In the last three sections we took a specific look at what it is you think you want why you want it and why you haven't already got it. These questions were very powerful and they enabled you to see things you may not have wanted to see. As much as we think we want something, it is often easier to stay stuck and come up with excuses for not being able to get what you really want. That is how victims remain as victims.

This may be the point at which you want to forget The Creating Game, put down this book and start something else. Don't do that. Stay with it and you will get past the self sabotaging patterns that you continually live with. One of the biggest reasons for giving up at this stage is that you are beginning to see that to get what you really desire you need to take responsibility for your actions, your life and your own well being. The Creating Game is absolutely up to you and no one else. This is a big moment and you will feel fear when you recognise this. You can do EFT at this stage;

'Even though I feel the fear of going forward, I love and accept myself completely'

You may also think about giving up because you've found that the things you thought you wanted are actually not that important and you lose motivation to go forward. There are two points to make here.

Firstly you should look at the true reason for changing your mind about your desires. Often when we get closer to something our self sabotaging voice says, "You cannot have that because you don't deserve it." If this is the case you should be able at this point in the game to be able to hear this inner voice and use EFT again;

'Even though I do not deserve…I love and accept myself completely'

The second point is that you have truly realised the original things you thought you desired have no draw on you anymore because this work has changed your perception. If this is the case then go back and ask yourself the question again. What do I think I want? After answering it make yourself a different list. If you find you are coming up with all the common excuses you made in previous chapters, go back, re-read and re-evaluate these points and notice if you have shifted your excuses, changed any, or come up with new ones. Accept that this is common for everyone and that it will fade through playing The Creating Game. Re-commit yourself to continue and, if you wish, practice EFT;

'Even though I have all these excuses that stop me, I love and accept myself completely'

## Focus Point

Close your eyes and take three, deep slow breaths and see yourself as already a magnificent creator. See yourself creating wonderful things for the world to see and experience. Don't hold back see what a difference you can make in the world? See how important you really are. Imagine yourself creating a better world in what ever way you would like to see it improved.

**INSIGHT** ( HOW DO YOU SABOTAGE YOURSELF? )

# You're the Best

The Creating Game works even if you do not believe in yourself, in what you do or what you can achieve. The Creating Game taps into the Laws of Attraction and is not selective or dependant on whether you think you are a good, bad, sincere or an inconsiderate person. Any beliefs about what you can have or deserve that depend upon what a good person you are do not apply to The Creating Game. These beliefs come from your past conditioning and have no meaning in this context. Regardless of whether you believe this or not the Creating Game will always be successful if you play by the rules. You will always get what you really want and this is happening already. The only problem is that you have been creating things unconsciously. The Creating Game helps you to understand the process of creating and guides you towards conscious, considered creation.

When you become aware of how you are creating you will see that it is your awareness about who you are and what you are choosing to be that will increase.

The key to creating is clarity. When you play The Creating Game you will come to understand that your mistakes, failings, poor behaviour, lack of success and your life patterns to date are simply a measure of the awareness you have brought to your life so far. As you become more aware you will understand that everything in your past was created because of how aware you were at that time. Until now you may not have understood certain factors about how you have created your life. As you continue, your awareness will expand, helping you to create your desires.

When you experience your life through the reactive feelings of good and bad you are driven by outside events, for example when you feel better because of what someone says, when being given a gift for 'being good', or the opposite, when you feel bad for speaking up to someone. Everyone has their own reactions to certain circumstances, based on how aware they are in a given situation. When you begin to understand that your reactions are often based upon conditioning from the past you can let go of your limiting habitual response and expand your own awareness. You will see that your reactions and how you behave based on those reactions are not who you choose to be, but who you have learnt to be. This awareness will enable you to change how you react and begin to have a conscious choice in your own behaviour. This is real creation in action. You will learn there is room for self forgiveness, that there is a way to change and create the life you can choose for yourself.

Start now by writing down all the areas where you are GREAT, all the times you know you have shown your greatness. Go ahead and take a deep breath, follow the simple inner voice guidelines and ask yourself 'Where do I shine, what is my greatness?'

There is no need to analyse this in any depth; your awareness is expanding every time you do these exercises, and they will help you to play The Creating Game faster and more successfully each time. Make a list of all the areas, where you are great. What are you great at? Just make a list and try not to limit your list or hold back.

Are you a great listener? Does your greatness show through your smile? Are you a great mother or father? Build up your own list and look for your own great attributes.

For many years before I was working with conscious creating I was unable and unwilling to believe I had done anything that would make me feel like a good mother, never mind a great mother. It was not until I became aware that whatever stopped me from believing I could have been good was based upon my perceptions at that time. I had done the best I could then, as a young mother. I had done all I could based on my own awareness. Now I would do things differently because I know so much more, but it was important for me to acknowledge that I did the best I could with the knowledge and awareness I had in those years. The same goes for you.

---

- ARE YOU A GREAT COOK?

- DO YOU SHINE AND SHOW YOUR GREATNESS WHEN YOU SING?

- ARE YOU GREAT AT YOUR JOB?

- ARE YOU A GREAT DANCER?

- ARE YOU A GREAT FRIEND?

- DOES YOUR BEAUTY SHINE?

- ARE YOU A GOOD LISTENER?

- DO YOU BELIEVE YOU ARE A WONDERFUL PARENT?

- ARE YOU A GREAT SON OR DAUGHTER?

- ARE YOU AN EXCELLENT TEACHER?

- ARE YOU A MODEL STUDENT?

- ARE YOU A GOOD NEGOTIATOR?

- DO YOU HELP OTHERS TO SOLVE PROBLEMS?

---

When you've built up a list, write in more detail about your greatness, be specific and give details. Why you think you are great in this area? How do you know you're great in this area?

Try to describe why you think you shine and show greatness. Notice how you feel and react and make some things seem small and less important than they really are and notice how you may have limited your list. As you go through the list see if it expands by working on it and if there are other areas where you are great.

As you become more aware of your self you will develop more objectivity and recognise other sides to what you may have seen as failings. You might now see greatness in some of your thoughts and actions. Look back and check that if by altering your perspective you might add more to your list. One client of mine constantly condemned himself for having no focus, for doing too many jobs at the same time and rarely getting them finished. As he became more aware he could see this made him great at multi tasking and once he shifted his viewpoint he recognised greatness and was able to use his ability in a more focussed way. What usually makes your 'problem' worse is the way you look at it and this is quite simply a product of awareness.

Consider some of the areas which you label as failings and see if you can turn them around and make them into your greatness attributes. Add them to your list

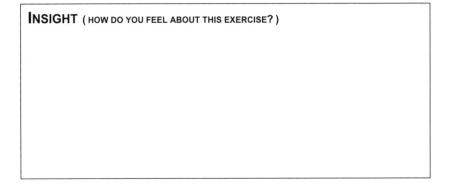

**Focus Point**

Close your eyes and take three, deep slow breaths. Imagine that you are telling some one how GREAT you really are. What would you say to them? Then what would you tell them about yourself? What do you intend to create in this world? Then add this affirmation and say it out loud. 'I am the most important, interesting, divine and creative person in my life', say it with meaning and let it penetrate and make you smile from the inside out.

INSIGHT ( HOW DO YOU FEEL ABOUT THIS EXERCISE? )

# I Am The Greatest

*"Act as if it were impossible to fail"*
## Dorothea Brandle

*"Act as if what you do makes a difference"*
## William Jones

*"Act as if you had already created your hearts desires"*
## Vani

# Awareness in Depth

You are really close to committing to a specific creation, the one you will be working with in the next three months as described in the opening pages of this book. Before you do, now is the time to bring yourself up to date on your overall awareness levels. You have been looking at awareness relating to your past and now you need to look at where you are today.

Before you begin take some slow deep breaths and place your full palm on your throat chakra, located behind your Adam's apple. Cup your hand around your throat and with your eyes closed commit to being truthful about where you are in your life right now. You are going to answer some questions that require total honesty and you might feel uncomfortable, but answering them will take you forward. The throat chakra is connected to your inner integrity. Many people who work with this exercise will find their throat being constricted, or a need to cough and clear the throat area. If this happens to you it is a good indication that you are connecting to your throat chakra and creating a space for honesty about yourself.

Keeping your eyes closed, your body calm and keeping your hand on your throat say the chakra chant ham (haaaaam). Say it several times allowing the sound of the chant to resonate in your throat. This is quite easy because the sound ham vibrates powerfully in the throat. Do this for a minute or for longer if you enjoy the sensations and then connect with your inner voice, go quiet and let your body relax. Ask yourself some reality questions from the list below.

1.      DO YOU ENJOY YOUR LIFE NOW?

2.      ARE YOU HAPPY WITH YOUR CURRENT JOB?

3.      DO YOU HAVE A LOVING AND HAPPY RELATIONSHIP?

4.      ARE YOU CONTENT WITH WHO YOU ARE?

5.      DO YOU HAVE MANY FRIENDS?

6.      DO YOU HAVE MANY DEBTS?

7.      HOW DO YOU GET ALONG WITH NEIGHBOURS?

8.      WHAT IS YOUR HEALTH LIKE?

9.      DO YOU GET ALONG WITH YOUR CHILDREN?

10.     ARE YOU CLOSE TO YOUR PARENTS?

11.     DO YOU FEEL FULFILLED?

Continued…

12.  WHAT DO YOU DO FOR FUN?

13.  DO YOU SMOKE?

14.  DO YOU DEPEND ON ALCOHOL, DRUGS, SEX?

15.  HOW DO YOU SOCIALISE?

16.  DO YOU LOVE YOUR SPOUSE?

17.  HOW MUCH ATTENTION DO YOU GIVE TO LOVED ONES?

18.  DO YOU PRAISE OTHERS?

19.  HOW MUCH COMPASSION DO YOU GIVE TO OTHERS?

20.  DO YOU LISTEN AND SHARE?

21.  DO YOU TAKE THE TIME TO UNDERSTAND OTHERS?

22.  HOW MUCH TIME DO YOU GIVE YOURSELF?

23.  HOW OFTEN DO YOU NURTURE YOUR BODY?

24.  HOW OFTEN DO YOU NURTURE YOUR SPIRIT?

---

This is the time to really look at where you are in your life today. Where you are right now is exactly as you created it and being absolutely clear and without judgement is a powerful step to creating. You must know where your reality sits in the context of the things that you want to create.

Consider the list of things you thought you wanted from the pages 'What Do You Think You Want' and look briefly at the discrepancy between what you say you want and how your actions are now affecting your actual outcomes. Here is a good example. Another client, John, wanted to create "being more affectionate" with his wife. When he looked at the reality of how he behaved towards her, John realised he was normally quite inconsiderate. He rarely did things that would stimulate affectionate behaviour. He rarely sat with her unless the TV was switched on and he was watching sport. Whilst she didn't complain, he knew she didn't enjoy it. John had chosen to ignore the fact that being more attentive might mean sacrificing football to watch something more conducive to create mutual feelings of affection.

John discovered that he actually wanted his wife to be more affectionate towards him, yet he rarely did things to stimulate affection. When he looked honestly at how a person might behave who was truly affectionate, he saw that he needed to become more aware so that he could show his wife he really wanted to be affectionate. He decided to ask her what it was he might need to do to show his affection. John received a wonderful list of ways to do this. By being honest and open enough to ask he got what he needed to manifest his creation.

Most people do not take the time to understand what they think they desire. Sometimes they discover that behind the desire is another motive. In John's case being more affectionate meant he needed to pay attention to his wife's idea of 'affectionate' and this required proper communication.

The difficulty with generalised creations as described earlier is they can be very hard to specify and creation requires absolute clarity. Wanting to be more affectionate requires a considerable amount of clarity because it is such a big concept. It requires specific actions. When John looked at this he saw his wish to be more affectionate involved many layers of desire. He saw that he wanted to receive affection as much as give it, but he was honest enough to realise that affection requires actions that build mutual trust. There is nothing wrong with any desire you may have but being global and general about them is one of the ways in which you stop yourself from actually achieving it.

Choosing a 3 month period within which to manifest your creation forces you to be clear with your intention. As you gain experience of creating you will discover that creating shorter concise projects increases self awareness and will open many doors to future successful creating.

A simple reality check can be done on the first question in my list, 'Do you enjoy your life?, a global question. If the answer is no then ask yourself why. Some people answer this question by saying 'I don't know why I don't enjoy life, it just sucks' and often with very simple questioning you can get closer to some valuable answers.

**Linda**    "Why don't you enjoy life?"

**Student**    "Because I don't go anywhere"

**Linda**    "Why don't you go anywhere?"

**Student**    "I haven't got any one to go any where with"

**Linda**    "Why haven't you got any one?"

**Student**    "I don't know, I don't seem to get on with people"

**Linda**    "Why is that?"

**Student**    "Well some people think I am a bit aggressive"

**Linda**    "Are you aggressive?"

**Student**    "Well sometimes people can be so damn awkward can't they?"

**Linda**    "Can they?"

**Student**    "Well yes they can"

**Linda**    "Ok so why not join a course and learn a new hobby?"

**Student**    "Well people can be awkward there can't they?"

**Linda**    "Do you think that you might be awkward also?"

**Student**    "Oh really? I hadn't thought of that!"

The reality is this student saw a mirror of her own awkwardness in other people and had been unable to see the way in which she'd chosen to ignore the judgements of people who she says are 'all awkward'. She could of course shift around and say she had nowhere to go and so on, until she exhausts her excuses. In this instance it leads to the student seeing the reality of where she is, what she is doing and what she may need to consider doing to enjoy life more. This leads to a much greater awareness that will encourage her to move in the areas she wants to create.

It might be that this student needs to see a counsellor as she continues to use other people's awkwardness to stop her from exploring new avenues. Or it is likely that this exercise will help her to see her own limitations and enable her to take baby steps and join a structured educational class.

Colin is another good example. On his list his desire was to be a professional golfer. His creation read 'I want to be golf pro'. By the time he had progressed to this part of The Creating Game he had become more aware about his desires and why. He realised that in reality he played golf three times a week which was high for some golfers but not enough to be golf pro. His desire was more about being recognised by his peers and one of the ways he felt he could do this was showing himself as a great golfer. He decided it wasn't a real desire and he was not prepared to spend any more time than three days a week playing golf. He would pay more attention to being a good friend to his peers and encouraging their performance and game, which he had ignored in his false desire. Several weeks later he called to say that his relationship with his golf friends had shifted enormously he felt loved and lovable because of his reality check.

Go through each item on your list and see which ones correspond in any way to your reality. Do a measure of how far from your creation you are today. Notice whether you do, say or have any behaviour patterns that are in alignment with what you say you want. Without spending too much time on your list just check whether any of your desires need to be removed because your awareness has increased, showing you that some things are really not what you want.

## Focus Point

Close your eyes and take three, deep slow breaths. Take one of the beliefs about yourself that you would like to change and bring it into your mind. Focus on it and change this belief into a belief that serves you in this creating journey. Imagine you have changed this belief from 'I am not good enough' to 'I am the best' and visualise your being 'the best'. In this internal place act out 'being the best' as though you were in a movie. Increase the sensations and enjoy the changes that are being made to your belief system. Accept this possibility as reality.

## INSIGHT ( HOW DO I FEEL IN A WORD?)

## AWARENESS IN DEPTH

ANSWER EACH QUESTION ON P.57 - 58 WITH YOUR PERSONAL NOTES

1. _____
2. _____
3. _____
4. _____
5. _____
6. _____
7. _____
8. _____
9. _____
10. _____
11. _____
12. _____
13. _____
14. _____
15. _____
16. _____
17. _____
18. _____
19. _____
20. _____
21. _____
22. _____
23. _____
24. _____

"Someone once said to the great golfer Arnold Palmer, after he had just won one of the Masters tournaments "Arnold you always seem to get lucky at just the right time and he replied 'Yep, and the more I practise the luckier I get'

Whatever you choose and whatever you do, consistency reaps the biggest rewards. The secret is to discover where you have consistently held yourself back and use your creative energy to consistently move yourself forwards"

*Jim Whitham*

# You Create Everything

Now you are going to make a choice. You are going to commit to one creation. Here are the main rules you must follow as you make your decision. You must be willing to commit to the list below and fill in your creation page with confirmations and statements that show you that you really do mean business.

- YOUR CREATION IS ABSOLUTELY CRYSTAL CLEAR

- YOU HAVE THREE MONTHS TO CREATE YOUR CREATION

- YOU LOVE THE IDEA OF HAVING IT

- THE CREATION IS FOR YOU

- YOUR CREATION DOES NOT DEPEND ON SOMEONE ELSE ALTHOUGH SOMEONE ELSE MAY BE INVOLVED

- YOUR CREATION IS NOT ABOUT CHANGING SOME ONE ELSE'S BEHAVIOUR

- WHEN YOU HAVE CHOSEN, YOU MUST BE WILLING TO COMMIT WHOLE HEARTEDLY

- NO MATTER WHAT HAPPENS YOU WILL REMAIN COMMITTED TO THIS CREATION

- YOU WILL NOT CHANGE YOUR CREATION DURING YOUR THREE MONTH PERIOD

- YOU WILL COMMIT TO THE CREATING GAME RULES.

- YOU HAVE WORKED THROUGH ALL THE PREVIOUS EXERCISES AND ACTIVITIES BEFORE YOU COME TO THIS POINT.

- AT LEAST FOR THE NEXT THREE MONTHS YOU WILL LET GO OF ANY PAST EXCUSES FOR NOT CREATING THIS CREATION. YOU CAN PICK UP YOUR EXCUSES AFTER THE THREE MONTHS.

- YOU WILL REAFFIRM YOUR CREATION EVERY DAY.

- YOU WILL BE OPEN TO HELP FROM OTHERS IF NEEDED DURING YOUR CREATION PERIOD.

- YOU WILL DO CONTINUAL APPRAISAL REGARDING YOUR CURRENT REALITY AND WHERE YOU ARE EACH DAY WITH YOUR CREATION. YOU WILL REINFORCE YOUR VISION OF YOUR COMPLETED CREATION.

## Focus Point

Close your eyes and take three, deep slow breaths and repeat slowly and intentionally, with your hand on your heart. 'I am a unique and precious creative being and I commit to my creation, here and now'

# Ready Steady Go

**Setting up your creation and creating intention and clarity.**

It is imperative that you are crystal clear about what your creation actually is. There must be no ambiguity about what you want to create. You must be passionate, excited, and love the idea of bringing it into existence. You may have nagging doubts as to whether you are worthy enough to have your desire or if you deserve it, but they are not relevant in The Creating Game. The Universe and the Law of Attraction have no selection process to keep you from your creation; only you do this, so ignore the nagging inner voice and simply get on with the Game . When you experience any uncertainties, fears or reservations take a breath and do a sequence of EFT saying 'Even though I have doubts about my ability to create, I love and accept myself completely' and then move on to your creating. Always come back to your actual creation, read it, visualise it and stay focussed with it.

It helps to be excited about what you are creating so choose something that really turns you on and become clear about it.

Whenever and however you falter, the necessary motivation will come from concentration and remembering to commit again and again to your creation. It does not matter how you have failed in the past or what your inner nagging voice says. It isn't relevant that you are inexperienced, because the creating process helps you to build that creative experience. Your only concern is to focus on your creation. When you clarify what that is you open all the doors for the universe to help you on your path. You are making it clear exactly what it is you desire. So go ahead and take a deep breath, follow the simple inner voice guidelines and make a choice about which item on your list you are going to focus on and create.

Select three creations from your list "What do I think I Want" and answer the following questions to achieve greater clarity.

WHAT DO WANT, WHAT DO YOU MEAN?

HOW WILL YOU KNOW EXACTLY WHEN YOU HAVE IT?

WHAT WILL YOU HAVE?

HOW WILL IT LOOK?

HOW WILL IT SOUND?

HOW WILL IT FEEL?

HOW WILL YOU KNOW YOU HAVE SUCCEEDED IN CREATING IT?

Narrow the choice to one and describe your chosen creation in full on "My Creation" page.

Many people want to create love, happiness, freedom and contentment and when I ask them to tell me how they will know they have created it, it can be very difficult for them to explain. Lack of clarity will stop your creation from being born. Here is a typical scenario.

**Student**   "I want to be happy"

**Linda**   "How will you know when you are happy?"

**Student**   "Well, I will feel happier"

**Linda**   "How will you know you feel happier?"

**Student**   "Because I will wake up in the morning and feel happy"

**Linda**   "So why do you not feel happy when you wake up now?"

**Student**   "I don't know I just feel unhappy"

**Linda**   "What do you feel unhappy about?"

**Student**   "Well, I have nothing to get up for"

**Linda**   "What about your job?"

**Student**   "Oh, I hate my job"

**Linda**   "So if you changed your job would you feel happier?"

**Student**   "Well yes, I would!"

Here is a classic example of not being clear about what you desire. In this case creating a new job would be a start to her feeling happier. Happiness is too global as a goal, even though it is a fine desire as a life creation. You are more likely to reach generalised life goals, peace, love, happiness, health and contentment by successfully working on your specific creations. The more you unravel your big requests and learn to produce manageable creations the closer you will get to living your life as you desire it to be.

Many people come to workshops wanting to create a new relationship or fall in love. Often this desire is based on a need rather than a healthy wish. And often this longing is intensified straight after a break up. People on the rebound rarely have healthy desires as so often they are trying to fill a lonely space. If they are willing to break down this request into clear shorter term projects they are more likely to build self esteem, self love and awareness. In this case planning to join a new group or creating a trip will bring new adventures that can often lead to the longer term desire being manifested. The effect of this learning and building process enables you to make better choices about a future partner based on a clearer understanding of who you are and what you really want and enjoy, rather than based upon neediness.

You must be absolutely clear to manifest and create. The most effective way to test this is to ask yourself how you will know you have completely created it. You must have something specific to show for it. Go through your list, make your decision and retest it until you have a creation that is so crystal clear and certain that anyone could ask you what it was and you would be able to tell them without a moment's hesitation.

Keep working on this until you can do this and notice the energy and motivation that increases from your clarity. As you are clarifying your creation you are setting up an intention. It is from this your creation will be realised. Each time you re-evaluate where you are in The Creating Game during these three months you will be reinforcing your intention to create. When you are clear and ready to commit to your creation you are going to set your intention.

Write down your creation clearly in the space provided and sit comfortably. Take three slow and even breaths and place the palm of your hand on your heart and state your commitment. See if you have any emotions, excitement, or sense of motivation and simply accept and acknowledge that you have committed to being a co-creator with the Universe and that you have set this is motion. Here are some intention statements to help you get started:

'My name is Jayne and on this day 10th July 2005, my intention is to be a size 12 by the end of my three month period.'

'My name is John and today my intention is to create a beautiful conservatory in my garden so that I can enjoy my garden and entertain friends, I will complete my creation by Aug 2005.'

'My name is Sue and I will create a short book of poetry by Aug 2005'

Be as clear as you can with your own statement. After setting your intention, the next step is to spend time clarifying your creation and adding the necessary details.

Be absolutely sure you can respond to each bullet point with total clarity. Finally, when you have spent a great deal of time on this, write your creating statement down clearly on the creating page and also several times on big pieces of paper. Write them on post it notes and stick them every where so that you see your creating statement every day.

## Focus Point

Close your eyes and take three, deep slow breaths. Imagine your creation in your mind and do not leave this focus point until you can see it manifested clearly and totally.

If your image is hazy, remain quiet, still and gently breathing as you inspire your senses. What does your creation look like? What's its shape? What's its colour? What's its size? What does it smell like, taste like, sound like? Go through your senses and capture your creation within your mind clearly.

# My Creation

**Clarify your intent by describing your creation in full.**

# Your Creation

Do not go any further into The Creating Game and expect to be able to succeed if you have not completed ALL the activities. Unless you are an accomplished conscious creator (and you would not be reading this book if you were) you will be wasting your time. Do not attempt to skip anything at all in this book.

I overheard one student who came to a Creating Game workshop saying "Oh, I've done all this stuff before". Her creation was to lose weight; she had done all of 'this stuff' before and she was still overweight!

Notice how you set up your self sabotage by wanting to skip any stage's in this game. It will not work and you will fail if you do. Each time you create you must go through all the activities and unwind all the self limiting beliefs and patterns that have stopped you in the past. Only when we work through every activity can we begin to unravel the complexities of each separate creation. You may have completely different beliefs about creating one thing rather than another. How is it that you are driving the car of your dreams but not in a relationship of your dreams for instance? Each time you move on through The Creating Game weeks, months and years will have passed, new experiences encountered, relationships could be different and your desires may change considerably. All external factors will affect your game.

If you truly believe its worth creating whatever you desire don't skimp. Follow the rules until you are proficient at The Creating Game.

## Focus Point

Close your eyes and take three, deep slow breaths and check for any stumbling blocks any sabotaging techniques you have discovered and redo the focus point on the last chapter

INSIGHT ( HOW DO YOU FEEL? )

# Accepting

Where are you today in relation to your specific creation? Look carefully at your creation and spend some time examining your current place in the process at this moment. If you have chosen to create a conservatory as John did in our earlier example, write down exactly what you have already done to achieve it, if anything.

In John's case he reinforced his commitment by writing down his intention statement. He had previously looked at some designs in magazines so he had an idea about what it would look like. He had already discussed the design and dimensions with his wife. He also knew how much it might cost and what he was willing to pay.

After John had looked at his current reality he accepted where he was and re-committed to his clear creation statement. This was an excellent time to do EFT and John worked on 'Even though I do not have my conservatory, I deeply and completely accept myself and my intention is to create a beautiful conservatory'

Every time John checks his current reality and uses EFT to clear any negative energy blocks or to simply confirm his intention to create, he opens the universal energy that propels all creations to manifest. This powerful process will enable John to look at what is required to create his desire, what he needs to sort out, what needs to be in place and what organisation is required. Each day that he focuses on his finished creation and looks at exactly where he is at this moment in its development he maintains clarity, vision and creative ability.

You must know two things to succeed in The Creating Game:

---

1.    KNOW WHAT YOU WANT

2.    KNOW WHERE YOU ARE

---

John's energy levels will increase and his motivation will lead him to do what is required to put into place the steps to create his conservatory. Each time John hits a block and has difficulty at any point, whether it is self doubt or any other excuses, he can use EFT on the blockage and also re-commit his intention clearly towards his creation.

You do not need to use EFT or any other of the tools that I have suggested throughout but it is vital to continue to read and commit to your creation again and again. It is however crucial that you work with the creation forms,

69

explained later, completing them regularly. Re-affirming your creation with absolute clarity is the single most important practice that you must master. At every setback go back to your creation forms and work through each section.

Use The Creating Game book and work with it on a weekly basis at the very minimum, filling in the sections continually and re-committing to your desired creation, again and again, using EFT each time you stumble.

Finally, act and talk as though you have already created your desire. Bring into your daily awareness the concept of success. Read books about your desire, go to places and experience your creation if you can, look at pictures and make a creation picture as described in the tools chapter. See it already created. Visualise its existence.

Trust that you are powerful and a creator and that your desires are already waiting. Commit yourself to filling in your action sheets regularly and monitoring your progress.

Accept that nothing or no one will stop you from your creation. Accept that you are great.

## Focus Point

Close your eyes and take three, deep slow breaths and affirm these commitments. Say each one out loud and separately, knowing and understanding that you and you alone are in charge of your commitment to your creation.

'I am completely responsible for my actions'
'I am a co-creator with the universe and this is reflected in my creating'
'I make the final decision in whether I consciously create or not'

Remind yourself of this focus everyday that you create.

---

**INSIGHT** ( WRITE DOWN A STATEMENT THAT SHOWS YOU ACCEPT YOU ARE READY? )

# The Wisdom Circle

The Creating Game Book came to me in a dream. It seemed that everything came together in a completeness that encompassed all my learning practices. I saw each chapter heading and its contents in a heartbeat. Actually writing the book took a little longer, but is was still driven forward by an energy that is created by the universe. Nothing would stop its manifestation.

I was driven by a wisdom circle although at the time I did not know it. As I was putting the last minute changes together and the book was completed I had another dream with another message. This happened whilst I was teaching at the Mandala Ashram in Wales. My dream showed me a wisdom circle in full practice and I was transported to another time and place where I learned the valuable gifts that are found in ancient wisdom circles. I demonstrated the process on the following day and myself and all involved were changed. I knew it needed to be included in The Creating Game.

I have explained the process on the next page and would ask you to use the wisdom circle knowing that you connect with the wisest sages of all time, with humility and reverence.

*Vani*

# The Wisdom Circle

The great wise sages of ancient times would come together in 'wisdom circles' and ask their Gods, wise ones, mentors, teachers and cherished family and friends to support them in their quests.

Prepare yourself to set up your own 'wisdom circle' to encourage support, love, forgiveness, understanding and excitement in your creation.

Make a list of all the people you would like to call upon to help you with your work. This list can include anyone, Gods, Jesus, Mother Earth, Old Father Time, Michelangelo, Elvis, saints, wise family members or friends.
You might want to consider who would be most appropriate to help you in this particular project. You may believe that Jesus would be perfect in your 'wisdom circle' to help you to forgive someone. Mother Theresa may provide you with unconditional compassion for yourself. Take your time to create your own 'wisdom circle' and also know that you can create new ones at any time. The secret to successful 'wisdom circles' is to ensure you have given enough time and significance to this tradition sacred practice.

When you have compiled your list of wise people go through each one, close your eyes, and imagine them in your mind. See each face and acknowledge their presence. Ask each person individually for their permission to be included into your circle. On this spiritual level you will always receive positive acceptance, even if you are guided to ask someone else who is considered more able to help this specific creation.

Prepare your circle by lighting a candle, play some soothing music and sit in a position to join your 'wisdom circle'. Be clear about your circle members and one by one imagine them joining you in holding hands in a circle. Do not be surprised if some one else joins you who you did not expect. Often family members who have passed on may want to help and this is perfectly fine.

When you are ready to speak tell your 'wisdom circle' what you want to create and why. Wait for any questions keeping the participants in your awareness. Ask specific questions about how you might achieve your desire, what advice can they provide. You may find that you are guided to forgive an old hurt or say a particular prayer every night. Although you may not think what is offered has much to do with your creation, you would be wise to follow the guidance and suggestions. If you do I can assure you that it will be valuable to your creating process. In this instance trust is a quality that you may be required to embrace.

# WISDOM CIRCLE 'GUIDES' AND MESSAGES.

# Creation Forms

At this stage in The Creating Game you will see the page is split into three sections and an example of how you can complete it is shown. This is an essential part of The Game.

In section one you must write down your creation statement clearly; in the second section you will write where you are now and in the third section you will write down what you need to do.

These forms will help you to stay very focussed.

---

- Remember that regardless of what is going on in your life it should not stop you from continuing to focus on your chosen creation.

- What ever you think, do or believe nothing will stop your creation, only you.

- The key is to continually focus on your creation and then look at where you are today with clarity and re-commit to your creation.

- Imagine it as you want it to be in detail and be enthused and excited

- Use all your senses of sight, touch, smell, taste and sound as you imagine your creation into existence.

- Look at the difference between what you desire and where you are now.

- Consider what you now need to do and make plans to carry this out.

- You have ample spaces to keep your creation forms flowing and up to date.

- Use the forms regularly so that you can see your progress.

- I have given you two examples to help you to see how the forms work

---

Happy creating!

| Date | My Creation | My Reality | What is Needed |
|---|---|---|---|
| Example 1 6/7/2005 | To have a beautiful designed bedroom that is practical | My bedroom is cluttered and full of junk | First to go through the rubbish and give stuff away that I don't want |
| Example 2 6/7/2005 | I want to have my hair restyled completed | Hair looks a mess. Needs cut, shape, coloured – not sure | Collect mags and pics of different styles. Start to consider what I like |
| | | | |
| | | | |
| | | | |
| | | | |
| | | | |
| | | | |

| Date | My Creation | My Reality | What is Needed |
|------|-------------|------------|----------------|
|      |             |            |                |
|      |             |            |                |
|      |             |            |                |
|      |             |            |                |
|      |             |            |                |
|      |             |            |                |
|      |             |            |                |
|      |             |            |                |

| Date | My Creation | My Reality | What is Needed |
|------|-------------|------------|----------------|
|      |             |            |                |
|      |             |            |                |
|      |             |            |                |
|      |             |            |                |
|      |             |            |                |
|      |             |            |                |
|      |             |            |                |

| Date | My Creation | My Reality | What is Needed |
|------|-------------|------------|----------------|
|      |             |            |                |
|      |             |            |                |
|      |             |            |                |
|      |             |            |                |
|      |             |            |                |
|      |             |            |                |
|      |             |            |                |
|      |             |            |                |

# Tools

If you work through The Creating Game book and do all the exercises you will be certain to have some amazing results. However, by including all or a selection of tools from the list below you will have a much greater chance of creating more effectively.

I have briefly described each tool and you can choose which ones feel most appropriate for you. Make a commitment to choose some of them and stay with them on a regular basis through out your creating.

- **Meditation:** WHEN YOU STOP, GO INSIDE AND CONNECT WITH YOUR INNER VOICE. THIS EXERCISE IS A FORM OF MEDITATION, WHICH PREPARES YOU AND HELPS YOU TO BE MORE RELAXED AND OPEN TO CHANGE. YOU MAY WANT TO PURCHASE A MEDITATION CD AND COMMIT TO SPENDING LONGER PERIODS OF QUIET TIME IN MEDIATION. IT IS PROVEN ACROSS ALL CULTURES THAT MEDITATION CREATES HEIGHTENED AWARENESS FOR ANY INDIVIDUAL. SEE WWW.THECREATINGGAME.COM FOR A CD I HAVE PRODUCED FOR THIS PURPOSE.

- **Creation Picture:** WHEN YOU HAVE DECIDED ON YOUR CREATION, COMPILE A SELECTION OF PICTURES AND WORDS FROM MAGAZINES OR NEWSPAPERS. CONSIDER ADDING SMALL BEAUTIFUL OBJECTS AND SHAPES THAT YOU CAN MAKE INTO A COLLAGE THAT WILL REMIND YOU AND REFLECT UPON YOUR CREATION. KEEP THIS IN VIEW EVERY DAY AND ADD TO IT AS YOU GET CLOSER TO MANIFESTING YOUR CREATION. HAVE FUN DOING IT.

- **EFT:** IN THE APPENDIX THERE IS A BRIEF DESCRIPTION OF GARY CRAIG'S EMOTIONAL FREEDOM TECHNIQUE. DO EFT EVERY SINGLE TIME YOU FEEL A DISTURBANCE IN YOUR ENERGY, BODY OR MIND. GARY TELLS HIS STUDENTS TO 'DO IT ON EVERYTHING'

- **Nutrition:** AFTER DOING THE ACTIVITY ON YOUR PHYSICAL HEALTH DETERMINE WHAT YOU NEED TO DO ABOUT YOUR NUTRITION. MAYBE YOU NEED TO CUT DOWN ON RED MEAT OR ALCOHOL AND NEED TO INCREASE ORGANIC HEALTHY FOODS. MAKE A COMMITMENT TO GIVE YOURSELF HEALTHY MEALS EVERY DAY. YOU COULD CONVERT THIS INTO THE CREATING GAME AND MAKE IT ONE OF YOUR CREATIONS!

- **Flower Essences:** ARE LIQUID PLANT, FLOWER AND TREE PREPARATIONS WHICH CARRY A POSITIVE UNIQUE MESSAGE OF HEALING FROM THE CHOSEN SPECIES. FLOWER ESSENCES GENTLY ENCOURAGE OUR PHYSICAL BODY AND OUR EMOTIONAL, SPIRITUAL AND MENTAL ASPECTS TO SELF-HEAL. THEY HELP YOU TO CLEAR EMOTIONAL TRAUMA FROM CELLULAR MEMORY AND WORK EXTREMELY WELL WITH EFT PRACTICES.

- **The Chakra System:** WHEN WE WORK WITH OUR CHAKRAS AND UNDERSTAND THEIR FUNCTIONING WE CAN EXPERIENCE AN OPENING, A DEVELOPING AND HARMONISING OF OUR ENERGY. CHAKRA CHANTING WILL ENABLE SELF AWARENESS AND SELF HEALING FOR THE BODY AND THE MIND. A NUMBER OF CDS AND BOOKS ARE AVAILABLE THAT PROVIDE DETAILED INFORMATION ON THE CHAKRA SYSTEM.

Continued…

- **Special Place:** GIVE YOURSELF A SPECIAL AND SACRED PLACE WHERE YOU CAN PRACTICE THE CREATING GAME, WHERE YOU CAN CHANT, PRAY AND MEDITATE. IT CAN BE A TABLE TOP, OR A CORNER IN A ROOM. ADD BEAUTIFUL OBJECTS, FLOWERS, FRAGRANCE AND CHAKRA COLOURS TO ENCOURAGE AND SUPPORT YOUR JOURNEY.

- **Nature:** SPEND PURPOSEFUL TIME IN NATURE AND NOTICE THE PERFECTION OF THE EVER CHANGING SEASONS AND THE BEAUTY AROUND YOU. CONNECT WITH YOUR SENSE OF SIGHT, SOUND, SMELL, TOUCH AND TASTE WHEN YOU GO FOR A WALK. FEEL THE FREEDOM OF YOUR INNER SPIRIT.

- **Breathing:** YOU ARE OFTEN REMINDED OF SLOW AND EVEN BREATHING THROUGHOUT THIS WORK. FOCUSSED BREATHING HELPS CONCENTRATION AND RELAXATION.

- **Movement / Dance:** TAKE ANY OPPORTUNITY TO MOVE AND DANCE TO SOFT, SLOW BALLADS AND FIERY, PASSIONATE MUSIC. PEOPLE RARELY DO SPONTANEOUS OR PURPOSEFUL MOVEMENT AND IT CAN BE A LIBERATING SENSATION FOR THE BODY AND MIND.

- **Post-It Notes:** WRITE OUT AS MANY NOTES YOU MAY NEED TO HELP TO REMIND YOU ABOUT YOUR CREATION AND THE TASKS YOU ARE WORKING WITH. STICK THEM ALL OVER YOUR HOME SO THAT YOU ARE CONSTANTLY REMINDED, EVERY DAY.

- **Sleep intention:** BEFORE YOU GO TO BED EACH NIGHT SET AN INTENTION TO REMAIN ON TRACK WITH YOUR CREATION. WRITE IT DOWN BEFORE YOU GO TO SLEEP AND PUT IT UNDER YOUR PILLOW. IMAGINE YOUR CREATION ALREADY IN EXISTENCE, ENCOURAGE YOUR DREAMING STATE AND CREATE IT IN YOUR SLEEP!

- **Qualities:** GO TO THE QUALITIES CHART AND CLOSE YOUR EYES. RANDOMLY PICK ONE OF THE QUALITIES TO WORK WITH FOR THIS CREATION. DO NOT CHANGE IT BECAUSE YOU DO NOT LIKE IT OR WOULD RATHER HAVE A DIFFERENT ONE. YOUR INNER PSYCHE WILL LEAD YOU TO THE CORRECT QUALITY. FOLLOW THE EXPLANATION ON THE QUALITY CHART.

---

**INSIGHTS** ( ABOUT USING THESE OR OTHER TOOLS )

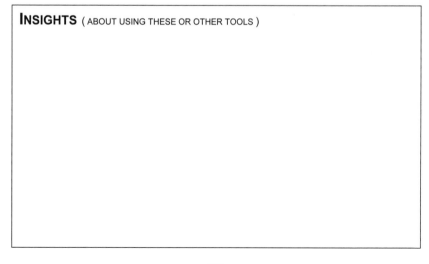

# Momentum

As you begin to get closer to your desired creation you are likely to feel a new surge of energy and a desire to start again over again with a new creation and The Creating Game. This is perfectly normal and exciting. You must be wary of diving into another separate game until you are absolutely clear and certain that your current creation is close to manifesting in its entirety. If you begin another game too soon you will fail and this will set up a momentum for not creating. Do not start a new creation until you are positive it is not about abandoning your current creation before it is completed.

Do not be fooled into falling back into the negative behaviour of your past or the nagging voice that says, 'Oh well, you don't really want it any more'. Go to the end, push the boundaries and use all the tools. More than anything keep committing to your creating statement. Continue to evaluate your reality and continue to accept where you are and reinforce where you are going. These are crucial times in The Creating Game and EFT can be a huge benefit to open your blocked energy channels encouraging you to triumph.

With The Creating Game you will achieve:

- Increased self esteem

- Higher self awareness

- A new understanding of your potential

- A new purpose in life

- You will be more relaxed

- Your energy levels will increase

- You will feel happier

- You will feel more contentment

- , You will believe in yourself

- You will be a creator

**Creating something else?**

Buy another book and re-visit every exercise for each new creation for at least twelve months. Keep a check and evaluate how quickly you create and how your understanding about what you truly want begins to crystallise each time.

Read through The Creating Game book and look back at everything you have entered and notice how you have changed. What you now understand about yourself. Notice your self esteem and your vitality.

Before you begin to create anything else get another of The Creating Game books to keep you on track. Give yourself and your creation the gift of starting from the beginning with new words, new beliefs, new energy and new insights.

**The Creating Game book will act as a journal and life long encyclopaedia of your creations making a wonderful collection to look back at and to pass onto your children.**

The Universe thinks you are worth it!

## Focus Point

Close your eyes and take three slow breaths and ask yourself if you have completed your creation in full. You may be very close to completing and the energy of creating is driving you forward to beginning a new creation.

Breathe and enjoy this energy and dwell on your creating ability. What could you have done better, how might you do your creating differently. Play with this energy and learn from it.

INSIGHT ( NEW IDEAS FOR CREATING )

# Gratitude

When you have manifested your creation celebrate your achievement and be thankful and grateful for your amazing power of creation.

*Gratitude gives you strength*
*Gratitude gives you courage*
*Gratitude helps you forgive*
*Gratitude expands your awareness*
*Gratitude softens your heart*
*Gratitude has enormous power to heal*
*Gratitude increases excitement*
*Gratitude encourages humility*
*Gratitude connects you to love*
*Gratitude removes obstacles*
*Gratitude propels you forward*
*Gratitude finds a way*

*Look for gratitude everywhere*

*Be Grateful for everyday*
*Be Grateful for the sunshine and rain*
*Be Grateful for your challenges and triumphs*
*Be Grateful for the tears and pain, laughter and joy*
*Be Grateful for the food you eat and air you breathe*
*Be Grateful for choices and creations past and present*
*Be Grateful for the teachers in your life*
*Be Grateful for every moment*
*Be Grateful for your life*

Gratitude will help you to move through The Creating Game with grace.

Every night before you go to sleep take a few minutes to write down at least three things about your day that you are grateful for.  Look for the wonder in your life and be Grateful

Say thank you

*Vani*

# Appendix 1

## Abbreviated instructions for The Basic Recipe of EFT

Emotional Freedom Technique
Founder Gary Craig – for more information visit the EFT website
www.emofree.com
Adapted from the EFT Manual

**The Discovery Statement:**

> "The cause of all negative emotions is a disruption in the body's energy system"

### Careful Caution

You are required to take complete responsibility for your own emotional and physical well being both during and after these instructions. EFT has not been proven clinically so therefore consider this work experimental.

Do not change any medication without expert help.

Always ask your physician or therapist for full support.

The Authors of The Creating Game and founders of EFT will not be held legally or morally responsible in the unlikely event of negative reactions.

### Please read the full instructions provided on www.emofree.com

EFT is a simple procedure that helps to eliminate and reduce all kinds of negative emotion.

EFT will also work for many physical problems.

EFT involves focussing on the problem at hand and tapping on meridian points on the body and hands.

EFT uses the same meridian points that are used in acupuncture.

The full Basic EFT Recipe consists of four ingredients, two of which are identical. They are:

1. The Set Up

2. The Sequence

3. The 9 Gamut Procedure – you should read the full EFT manual for a comprehensive explanation of the Gamut point.

4. The Sequence

Tapping is done by using the index and middle finger pads.
Tap for about 7 times on each point, tapping quickly.
Tap firmly to feel the vibration of the tap, but do not hurt yourself.
The only point you will rub is the 'sore spot'.

## (1) The Set Up Statement

While you rub the 'sore spot' you will make a statement that describes and tunes into the problem

'Even though I procrastinate at work, I love and accept myself completely
'Do not worry about your set-up statement, think about your problem and say your statement out loud. Make your statement in your own language and do not try to make it sound better: 'Even though I am sick to death of John, I love and accept myself completely'.

You follow the set-up statement with a reminder phrase that keeps things easy and simple for you, but also keeps you focussed on the problem. If you're set up statement was 'Even though I am sick to death of John, I love and accept myself completely' your reminder phrase might be 'sick of John'.

Check how you are doing with your problem and give the problem a number at the outset. Ask yourself how intense it is for you. Ten is very intense and 0 is not at all intense. In this case if you are very angry at John and you are feeling very intense, you would measure 10. When you have done the EFT sequence check again to measure how much you have reduced in intensity.

## (2) Quick EFT Sequence Guide

i.    The set up - repeat 3 times: "Even though I _ _ _ _ _ _ _ _ I deeply and completely accept myself." Whilst rubbing the 'sore spot'.

ii.    The Tapping sequence – tap about 7 times on each point: EB, SE, UE, UN, Ch, CB, UA, Th, IF, MF, BF, KC.

iii.    The Gamut Procedure - continuously tap on the Gamut Point whilst you perform these 9 actions.

    1. Eyes closed
    2. Eyes open
    3. Eyes hard down right
    4. Eyes hard down left
    5. Roll eyes in circle
    6. Roll eyes in other direction
    7. Hum a song for 2 seconds
    8. Count to 5
    9. Hum a song for 2 seconds

iv.    Repeat the Sequence again – tap about 7 times on each point as number 2 above.

That's it in a nutshell. Sounds strange but it really works!

For EFT training in the UK contact Kay Gire at www.nivana-life.com

# (3) The Points

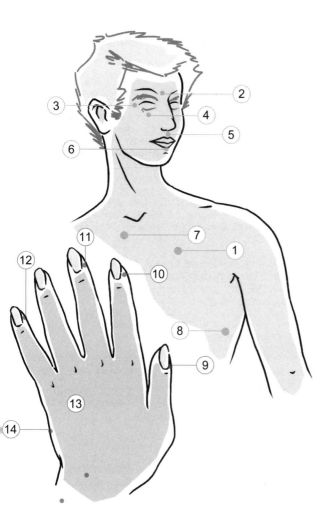

**1. Sore Spot**
Left hand side of chest, midway between armpit crease and centre of chest. There may be several sore spots in this region.

**2. Eyebrow**
Beginning of the eyebrow, above and slightly to the side of the nose.

**3. Side of eye**
Outer corner on the boney ridge.

**4. Under eye**
Directly beneath on bony ridge.

**5. Under nose**
Centrally between nose and upper lip.

**6. Chin**
Centrally under bottom lip.

**7. Collarbone**
One inch to the side of the central indent.

**8. Underarm**
Four inches below armpit on side of body.

**9. Thumbnail**
Side of thumb at base of nail.

**10. Index nail**
Side of index finger at base of nail.

**11. Middle nail**
Side of middle finger at base of nail.

**12. Little nail**
Side of lttle finger at base of nail.

**13. Side of hand**
Halfway down side of hand.

**14. Back of hand**
Once inch behind third and fourth knuckles.

# Appendix 2. The Chakras

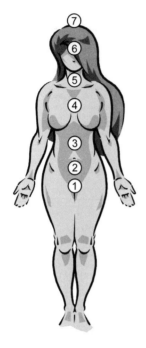

There are hundreds of good books and websites on chakras and below is a very brief description of the chakra system

Chakra means 'wheel' or 'vortex' in Sanskrit. The chakras can be described as 'balls' of energy, which are situated throughout the body. Each Chakra represents and interprets physical and emotional energy. According to ancient teachings there are many chakras in the body but the most well known are the seven 'main' ones that we are more familiar with.

These Seven chakras interact with the body's endocrine and nervous system and each chakra is associated with a particular part of the body. All our senses, emotions, feelings, perceptions and awareness can be experienced within the seven chakras.

Once you are aware of your chakra system you can work to release pain, pent up emotions, nervousness and improve your sense of well being. Learning the chakra chanting which is known as 'seed' sounds can help.

### The Seven Chakras

1. THE ROOT CHAKRA IS CONCERNED WITH OUR SENSE OF SECURITY AND SURVIVAL AND OUR SENSE OF BELONGING. THE SEED SOUND IS LAM.

2. THE SACRAL CHAKRA IS ASSOCIATED WITH DESIRE, SENSUALITY, AND SEXUALITY AND WHAT THE BODY WANTS AND NEEDS. THE SEED SOUND IS VAM.

3. THE SOLAR PLEXUS CHAKRA IS CONNECTED TO OUR WILLPOWER. IT IS CONCERNED WITH RELATIONSHIPS, POWER AND CONTROL. THE SEED SOUND IS RAM.

4. THE HEART CHAKRA IS CONNECTED TO LOVE, COMPASSION AND OUR PERCEPTION OF SELF LOVE. THIS CHAKRA IS A BRIDGE TO OUR HIGHER SELVES. SEED SOUND IS YAM.

5. THE THROAT CHAKRA IS ASSOCIATED WITH COMMUNICATION, HONESTY, LISTENING AND INTEGRITY TO ONESELF AND OTHERS. THE SEED SOUND IS HAM.

6. THE THIRD EYE CHAKRA IS ASSOCIATED WITH PERCEPTION, INTUITION, PSYCHIC ABILITIES AND INNER WISDOM. THE SEED SOUND IS SHAM.

7. THE CROWN CHAKRA CONNECTS US TO THE DIVINE ENERGY OF THE UNIVERSE AND OUR UNION WITH 'SPIRIT'. THE SEED SOUND IS AUM.

# Appendix 3. Qualities

If you would like to work with the qualities concept then follow these guidelines. Either write down each quality on a separate small piece of paper and fold them put them in a container and pull one out, or run you finger along the page, with your eyes closed and stop at one.

**Then follow these steps:**

- CLOSE YOUR EYES.

- TAKE THREE DEEP BREATHS.

- CHOOSE ONE OF THE QUALITIES AT RANDOM, LETTING YOUR INNER SELF MAKE THE CHOICE.

- STAY WITH THE FIRST QUALITY AND DO NOT SWAP IT BECAUSE YOU MIGHT NOT LIKE IT.

- SPEND SOME TIME CONSIDERING WHAT YOUR QUALITY MEANS TO YOU AND HOW IT AFFECTS YOU EMOTIONALLY.

- LOOK AT A THESAURUS OR LOOK ON THE INTERNET AND ENQUIRE ABOUT WHAT YOUR QUALITY MEANS AND REPRESENTS.

- CHOOSE TO COMMIT TO USING THE ATTRIBUTES AND MEANINGS OF YOUR QUALITY TO HELP YOU TO WORK WITH YOUR CREATION.

- FOR EXAMPLE IF YOUR QUALITY IS 'BEAUTY' PERFORM YOUR ACTIVITIES WITH THIS QUALITY IN YOUR MIND AND SPEND EVERY DAY CONSIDERING WHAT EFFECT YOUR QUALITY HAS ON YOUR LIFE AND YOUR CREATION. WITH 'BEAUTY' AS YOUR QUALITY HOW DO YOU SEE THE WORLD WHEN YOU WAKE UP IN THE MORNING? SEE IT THROUGH THE EYES OF BEAUTY. IF YOUR CREATION IS TO WRITE A POEM HOW WOULD THE QUALITY OF 'BEAUTY' AFFECT YOUR WORDS? IF YOUR CREATION TO DECORATE A NEW BEDROOM WHAT WOULD THE QUALITY OF 'BEAUTY' ENABLE YOU TO DO?

- WHATEVER QUALITY YOU HAVE BEEN GUIDED TO CHOSE BE ASSURED THAT IT WILL BE ABSOLUTELY CORRECT FOR YOU IN THIS CREATION.

| | |
|---|---|
| Beauty | Enthusiasm |
| Honest | Energetic |
| Determined | Humility |
| Persistence | Faith |
| Integrity | Trust |
| Peace | Forgiveness |
| Compassion | Generosity |

# Linda Bio

Linda (Vani is Linda's spiritual name) has a B.A in Communication and Psychology and has studied Integrative Coaching with the Debbie Ford Institute in San Diego, California. She is a Dr Bach mentor and practitioner, an Ayurvedic Trainer and Consultant and an Emotional Therapy Practitioner (EFT). She is currently developing her work in the sphere of Integrative Psychotherapy.

Linda has designed and delivered a series of successful workshops in the USA and the UK, including "Entering the Light" and "The Creating Game", "Making a Difference" and "Dosha for Life - understanding Ayurveda". She motivates those around her with high levels of energy and commitment and has brought this approach to workshops at Neal's Yard, the leading high street holistic retailer and the Mandala Yoga Ashram, a prestigious retreat in South Wales. She works with many clients providing intensive therapy and counselling on an individual basis.

She teaches that we create our lives on a daily basis: we all have real creative energy but most of the time we are not conscious of it and too often we use the energy wastefully, in thoughts and actions that trap us in negative states. Linda shows how we can shift our personal energy and create powerful changes within our lives.

Linda has been given the gift of 'healing energy' which she uses during her workshops and with individuals bringing about deep self awareness. She encourages people to examine themselves and the pains and rigours of their lives, to develop clarity with regard to their daily patterns of nutrition and complimentary activities and from there to develop an in-depth understanding of their health, happiness and wellbeing.

Find us on the web for more details of The Creating Game © Workshops and Individual Sessions go to:

**Home Page:**    www.thecreatinggame.com

**Email:**    info@thecreatinggame.com

**Telephone:**    01925 652 435

*May every dream that you have ever dreamed*
*May every desire that you have ever had*
*May every love that you have ever sought*
*May every ambition that you have ever had*
*May every hope that you have ever hoped*
*May every vision that you have ever seen*
*May every fantasy that you have ever imagined*
*May every love that you have always deserved*

*May all these things that are yours by right*
*Be created by you in this game of life that we all play!*

*Much love…*

*Vani*

My deepest gratitude to the wonderful teachers who taught
me to look at myself and love what I found.
To my children Carmen, Philip & Paul, I express my profound
love and thank you for touching my life as you do.
Many thanks to two of my greatest teachers Steve Crowe and Jim Whitham,
whom I chose in another place and time to show me who I was.
My appreciation goes to Lisa Rudd my dear spiritual sister who has unfailingly supported me
throughout many challenges which I 'remembered' were my own creations.
To Dave & Debbie Charlton and my surrogate family in Ashville I thank you for your
wonderful hospitality and friendship, promotion and support.
To Jo and Steve St Clair who helped me to find my purpose, taught me that I was a messenger
in this life and reminded me of my ego – thank you dear teachers.